PRENTICE HALL
LITERATURE
Timeless Voices, Timeless Themes

VIRGINIA

Virginia Standards of Learning Test Preparation Workbook

Virginia

**COPPER LEVEL
6TH GRADE**

PEARSON

Prentice
Hall

Boston, Massachusetts
Upper Saddle River, New Jersey

Pearson Prentice Hall™ is a trademark of Pearson Education, Inc.
Pearson® is a registered trademark of Pearsonplc.
Prentice Hall® is a registered trademark of Pearson Education, Inc.

ISBN 0-13-131328-2

6 7 8 9 10   08

Table of Contents

Copper Level Skills Practice

Practice Tests

About This Book

The **Virginia Standards of Learning Preparation Workbook** is designed to prepare you for the tests that are part of the Standards of Learning Testing Program. In the middle grades, you will take the English: Reading/Literature and Research SOL Test, the English: Writing SOL Test, and you may be required to take the ITBS, TerraNova, or SAT 10. With strong foundational skills that this workbook aims to refine, you can expect to apply your knowledge in testing situations, in your daily schoolwork, and in real life.

To this end, the **Virginia Standards of Learning Preparation Workbook** contains two parts: Skills Practice support for the *Timeless Voices, Timeless Themes* literature textbook; and Practice Tests, which provide opportunities to see your reading and language skills in action. The Practice Tests include the English: Reading/Literature and Research and Writing Tests, ITBS, TerraNova, and SAT 10.

The **Virginia Standards of Learning Preparation Workbook** approaches reading comprehension, grammar, and writing skill-building from three directions:

1. You can begin with Part 1 and practice each type of skill before attempting the Practice Tests.

2. Another approach is to begin with the Practice Tests in Part 2 and determine from results exactly which skills need refining.

3. Finally, because each item on the SOL Practice Tests is correlated to a related Standard of Learning, you can use the correlation to focus on refining specific skills.

However you choose to use the **Virginia Standards of Learning Preparation Workbook**, its purpose is to provide you with the tools to help you toward your best possible performance on all standardized tests for language arts.

VA Practice Test Report:
Reading/Literature and Research

Virginia Standards of Learning	Test Item(s)
REPORTING CATEGORY: Understand a variety of printed materials/resource materials.	
Grade 6 SOLs in This Reporting Category:	
6.3 The student will read and learn meanings of unfamiliar words.	
a) Use knowledge of word origins and derivations.	Sample A, 4
b) Identify analogies and figurative language.	Sample B, 1, 5
c) Use context and sentence structure to determine meanings and differentiate among multiple meanings of words.	14
d) Use word reference materials.	30
6.5 The student will read and demonstrate comprehension of a variety of informational selections.	
a) Identify questions to be answered.	9
b) Make, confirm, or revise predictions as needed.	10, 19
c) Use context to determine meanings of unfamiliar words and technical vocabulary.	Sample A, 7
d) Draw conclusions and make inferences based on explicit and implied information.	6, 12, 13, 15, 17, 23, 26, 29, 32
f) Compare and contrast information about one topic contained in different selections.	16
g) Select informational sources appropriate for a given purpose.	11
Grade 7 SOLs in This Reporting Category:	
7.4 The student will read to determine the meanings and pronunciations of unfamiliar words and phrases.	
a) Use roots and affixes to expand vocabulary.	Sample A, 4
b) Recognize analogies and figurative language.	Sample B, 1, 5
7.6 The student will read and demonstrate comprehension of a variety of informational texts.	
a) Use knowledge of text structures to aid comprehension.	2, 8, 25, 28
c) Distinguish fact from opinion in newspapers, magazines, and other print media.	21, 27
d) Identify the source, viewpoint, and purpose of texts.	6, 9
e) Describe how word choice and language structure convey an author's viewpoint.	12, 15
f) Summarize what is read.	10, 13, 18
7.7 The student will apply knowledge of appropriate reference materials.	
a) Use print and electronic sources to locate information in books and articles.	11
b) Use graphic organizers to organize information.	8, 31
Grade 8 SOLs in This Reporting Category:	
8.3 The student will analyze mass media messages.	
a) Evaluate the persuasive technique being used.	16
b) Describe the possible cause-effect relationships between mass media coverage and public opinion trends.	32

Virginia Standards of Learning	Test Item(s)
c) Evaluate sources, including advertisements, editorials, and feature stories, for relationships between intent and factual content.	9, 11, 16
8.4 The student will apply knowledge of word origins, derivations, inflections, analogies, and figurative language.	
a) Identify simile, metaphor, personification, hyperbole, and analogy.	Sample B, 1, 5
b) Use context, structure, and connotations to determine meaning of words and phrases.	Sample A, 14
8.6 The student will read, comprehend, and analyze a variety of informational sources.	
a) Draw on background knowledge and knowledge of text structure to understand selections.	8, 17, 19, 23
d) Analyze details for relevance and accuracy.	22, 32
e) Read and follow instructions to complete an assigned task.	29
h) Draw conclusions based on explicit and implied information.	23
i) Make inferences based on explicit and implied information.	6, 24, 26, 32

REPORTING CATEGORY: Understand elements of literature.

Grade 6 SOLs in This Reporting Category:

6.4 The student will read and demonstrate comprehension of a variety of fiction, narrative nonfiction, and poetry.	
a) Identify the elements of narrative structure, including setting, character, plot, conflict, and theme.	17, 35
b) Use knowledge of narrative and poetic structures to aid comprehension and predict outcomes.	17, 19
c) Describe the images created by language.	33, 34, 36
d) Describe how word choice and imagery contribute to the meaning of a text.	34, 40
f) Use information stated explicitly and implicitly in the text to draw conclusions and to make inferences.	6, 17
g) Explain how character and plot development are used in a selection to support central conflict or story line.	20

Grade 7 SOLs in This Reporting Category:

7.5 The student will read and demonstrate comprehension of a variety of fiction, narrative nonfiction, and poetry.	
a) Describe setting, character development, plot structure, theme, and conflict.	2, 17, 35
b) Compare and contrast forms, including short stories, novels, plays, folk literature, poetry, essays, and biographies.	
c) Describe the impact of word choice, imagery, and poetic devices.	33, 34, 36–40
d) Explain how form, including rhyme, rhythm, repetition, line structure, and punctuation, conveys the mood and meaning of a poem.	36, 40

Grade 8 SOLs in This Reporting Category:

8.5 The student will read and analyze a variety of narrative and poetic forms.	
a) Explain the use of symbols and figurative language.	5, 33
b) Describe inferred main ideas or themes, using evidence from the text as support.	6, 7, 34, 38, 39

Virginia Standards of Learning	Test Item(s)
c) Describe how authors use characters, conflict, point of view, and tone to create meaning.	3, 20, 35, 39
d) Compare and contrast the use of poetic elements of word choice, dialogue, form, rhyme, rhythm, and voice.	36–39
Grade 8 SOLs in This Reporting Category:	
8.8 The student will edit writing for correct grammar, capitalization, punctuation, spelling, sentence structure, and paragraphing.	
b) Use and punctuate correctly varied sentence structures to include conjunction and transition words.	Sample B
c) Choose the correct case and number for pronouns in prepositional phrases with compound objects.	18
d) Maintain consistent verb tense across paragraphs.	9, 15, 16
e) Use comparative and superlative degrees in adverbs and adjectives.	8

Test Score _____

Student Comments: _____

_____

_____

_____

_____

_____

_____

Parent Comments: _____

_____

_____

_____

_____

_____

_____

_____

Teacher Comments: _____

_____

_____

_____

_____

_____

_____

_____

VA Practice Test Report: Writing

Virginia Standards of Learning	Test Item(s)
REPORTING CATEGORY: Plan, compose, and revise writing in a variety of forms for a variety of purposes.	
Grade 6 SOLs in This Reporting Category:	
6.6 The student will write narratives, descriptions, and explanations.	
a) Use a variety of planning strategies to generate and organize ideas.	Sample A, 1, 2
b) Establish central idea, organization, elaboration, and unity.	12, 13
c) Select vocabulary and information to enhance the central idea, tone, and voice.	11, 14
d) Expand and embed ideas by using modifiers, standard coordination, and subordination in complete sentences.	6, 7
e) Revise writing for clarity.	Sample B, Sample C, 4, 17, 18
Grade 7 SOLs in This Reporting Category:	
7.8 The student will develop narrative, expository, and persuasive writing.	
a) Apply knowledge of prewriting strategies.	Sample A, 1, 2
b) Elaborate the central idea in an organized manner.	12, 13
c) Choose vocabulary and information that will create voice and tone.	11, 14
d) Use clauses and phrases to vary sentences.	19
e) Revise writing for clarify and effect.	Sample B, Sample C, 4, 17, 18
Grade 8 SOLs in This Reporting Category:	
8.7 The student will write in a variety of forms, including narrative, expository, persuasive, and informational.	
a) Use prewriting strategies to generate and organize ideas.	Sample A, 1, 2
b) Organize details to elaborate the central idea.	12, 13
c) Select specific vocabulary and information.	11, 14
d) Revise writing for word choice, sentence variety, and transitions among paragraphs.	Sample B, Sample C, 4, 17, 18
REPORTING CATEGORY: Edit for correct use of language, capitalization, punctuation, and spelling.	
Grade 6 SOLs in This Reporting Category:	
6.7 The student will edit writing for correct grammar, capitalization, punctuation, spelling, and sentence structure.	
b) Use subject-verb agreement with intervening phrases and clauses.	19
c) Use pronoun-antecedent agreement to include indefinite pronouns.	3, 10
d) Maintain consistent tense inflections across paragraphs.	9, 15, 16
e) Choose adverbs to describe verbs, adjectives, and other adverbs.	8
f) Use correct spelling for frequently used words.	5

Virginia Standards of Learning	Test Item(s)
Grade 7 SOLs in This Reporting Category:	
7.9 The student will edit writing for correct grammar, capitalization, punctuation, spelling, sentence structure, and paragraphing.	
c) Choose pronouns to agree with antecedents.	3, 10
d) Use subject-verb agreement with intervening phrases and clauses.	19
e) Edit for verb tense consistency.	9, 15, 16

Test Score _____

Student Comments: _____

_____

_____

_____

_____

_____

_____

_____

_____

Parent Comments: _____

_____

_____

_____

_____

_____

_____

_____

_____

Teacher Comments: _____

_____

_____

_____

_____

_____

_____

_____

_____

Reading Comprehension

Context Clues

Read the passage, and then answer the questions below it. Mark the letter of your answer on a bubble sheet if your teacher provides one; otherwise, circle the letter of the correct answer.

It was June and long past time for buying the special shoes that were quiet as a summer rain falling on the walks. June and the earth full of <u>raw</u> power and
  1
everything everywhere in motion. The grass was still pouring in from the country, <u>surrounding</u> the sidewalks, <u>stranding</u> the houses. Any moment the town would
2   3
capsize, go down and leave not a stir in the clover and weeds. And here Douglas stood, trapped on the dead cement and the red-brick streets, <u>hardly</u> able to
                                                                        4
move. . . .

Somehow the people who made tennis shoes knew what boys needed and wanted. They put marshmallows and <u>coiled</u> springs in the soles . . .
                                                    5
—"The Sound of Summer Running" by Ray Bradbury

---

1 In this passage the word <u>raw</u> means—
  A not cooked
  B not healed
  C not tamed
  D not natural

2 In this passage the word <u>surrounding</u> means—
  A destroying
  B encircling
  C protecting
  D piling

3 In this passage the word <u>stranding</u> means—
  A rescuing
  B betraying
  C isolating
  D burning

4 In this passage the word <u>hardly</u> means—
  A barely
  B exactly
  C completely
  D easily

5 In this passage the word <u>coiled</u> means—
  A dead
  B curled
  C rusty
  D magical

Reading Comprehension

Context Clues

Read the passage, and then answer the questions below it. Mark the letter of your answer on a bubble sheet if your teacher provides one; otherwise, circle the letter of the correct answer.

Because the roads would be too bad for travel for many days, Mr. Lacey couldn't get out to take the puppy to the pound in the city right away. He agreed to let it sleep in the basement while Mrs. Lacey grudgingly[1] let Doris feed it table scraps. The woman was <u>sensitive</u> about throwing out food.
                                               1

By the looks of it, Doris figured the puppy was about six months old, and on its way to being a big dog. She thought it might have some <u>shepherd</u> in it. . . .
                                                                2

Even after a week had gone by, Doris didn't name the dog. She knew her parents wouldn't let her keep it, that her father made so little money any pets were out of the question, and that the pup would <u>definitely</u> go to the <u>pound</u>
                                                          3   4
when the weather cleared. . . .

1. grudgingly, *adv.*: In an unenthusiastic or resentful way

—"Stray" by Cynthia Rylant

---

1 In the passage the word <u>sensitive</u> means—
   A relaxed
   B eager
   C indifferent
   D touchy

2 In the passage the word <u>shepherd</u> means—
   A one who guides sheep
   B a pastor
   C a breed of dog
   D a messenger

3 In the passage the word <u>definitely</u> means—
   A with pleasure
   B without reason
   C without doubt
   D with difficulty

4 In the passage the word <u>pound</u> means—
   A thump firmly
   B a weigh station
   C a unit of weight
   D a place for sheltering animals

Name _____ Class _____ Date_____

Reading Comprehension
Context Clues

Read the passage, and then answer the questions below it. Mark the letter of your answer on a bubble sheet if your teacher provides one; otherwise, circle the letter of the correct answer.

Diana Chang found her "voice" in other art forms as well as in poetry: fiction
              1   2

writing and painting. She has written novels, like *The Frontiers of Love*, and has

exhibited her paintings in art galleries.
3   4

Her poem "Saying Yes" is about Diana Chang's struggle to express her dual
                                                          5

identity as a Chinese American. Through the poem's question-and-answer format,
                                                       6

its brief lines, and simple words, the speaker conveys pride in being able to claim
                                                    7

two heritages.
   8

---

1 In the passage the word voice means—
  A sound vibration
  B expression
  C singing
  D complaining

2 In the passage the word fiction means—
  A based on true events
  B from the imagination
  C futuristic
  D technological

3 In the passage the word exhibited means—
  A displayed
  B destroyed
  C created
  D purchased

4 In the passage the word galleries means—
  A newspapers
  B theaters
  C buildings housing artwork
  D long, narrow passages

5 In the passage the word dual means—
  A combined
  B blended
  C concerned
  D consisting of two parts

6 In the passage the word format means—
  A arrangement
  B rhythm
  C contest
  D session

7 In the passage the word conveys means—
  A ignores
  B communicates
  C rescues
  D carries

8 In the passage the word heritages means—
  A inherited traditions
  B parents
  C inherited fortunes
  D family trees

Reading Comprehension

Context Clues

Read the passage, and then answer the questions below it. Mark the letter of your answer on a bubble sheet if your teacher provides one; otherwise, circle the letter of the correct answer.

"I guess they teachin' her somethin' <u>worthwhile</u> up there at Greensboro,"
                                      1

Grandpa Jeremiah said to Sister Todd. "I sure don't see what it is, though."

"You ain't never had no book learning, Jeremiah," Sister Todd shot back. She

wiped at where a <u>trickle</u> of sweat made a little path through the white dusting
                   2

powder she put on her chest to keep cool. "Them old ways you got ain't got

nothing for these young folks."

                    —"Jeremiah's Song" by Walter Dean Myers

There is no such thing as talent. If there are any <u>inborn</u>, God-given gifts, they
                                                    3

are in the precocious[1] fields of music, mathematics, and chess; if you have such a

gift, you know it by now. All the rest of us, in all the other fields, are not talented.

We all start out <u>dull</u> and weary and uninspired.[2]
                 4

1. precocious, *adj.*: Showing more ability than usual at one's age
2. uninspired, *adj.*: Without bright and original ideas

                    —"Talent" by Annie Dillard

---

1 In the passage the word <u>worthwhile</u> means—
  A useless
  B valuable
  C foreign
  D fashionable

2 In the passage the word <u>trickle</u> means—
  A filter
  B small flow
  C flood
  D spot

3 In the passage the word <u>inborn</u> means—
  A natural
  B expensive
  C learned
  D difficult

4 In the passage the word <u>dull</u> means—
  A dim
  B tarnished
  C energetic
  D gifted

Reading Comprehension

Context Clues

Read the passage, and then answer the questions below it. Mark the letter of your answer on a bubble sheet if your teacher provides one; otherwise, circle the letter of the correct answer.

In 1922, an Egyptologist[1] named Howard Carter discovered a buried staircase

that led to a <u>sealed</u> tomb. When the tomb was opened, Carter found <u>fantastic</u>
          1   2

treasures—items made of gold, alabaster, ebony, and precious stones. The

mummified body of King Tutankhamen, the 18-year-old boy king, had been

carefully preserved and buried with jewelry and other items that <u>indicated</u> his
                                                   3

importance. He had clearly been of <u>noble</u> birth.
                                  4

1. Egyptologist, *n.*: A student of Egypt

---

1 In the passage the word <u>sealed</u> means—
- **A** open
- **B** missing
- **C** tightly closed
- **D** damp

2 In the passage the word <u>fantastic</u> means—
- **A** worthless
- **B** hideous
- **C** marvelous
- **D** ghostly

3 In the passage the word <u>indicated</u> means—
- **A** minimized
- **B** diminished
- **C** ridiculed
- **D** pointed out

4 In the passage the word <u>noble</u> means—
- **A** difficult
- **B** upper-class
- **C** recent
- **D** lower-class

Reading Comprehension
Context Clues

Read the passage, and then answer the questions below it. Mark the letter of your answer on a bubble sheet if your teacher provides one; otherwise, circle the letter of the correct answer.

Evidently the men had agreed with their leader, for Walt Masters could hear
1
nothing but the rattle of the tin dishes which were being washed. Peering out

cautiously, he could see the leader studying a piece of paper. Walt knew what it
2
was at a glance—a list of all the unrecorded claims on Mazy May. Any man could

get these lists by applying to the gold commissioner at Dawson. . . .
3
Walt lay in the snow, thinking rapidly. He was only a boy, but in the face of the
4
threatened injustice to old lame Loren Hall he felt that he must do something. He
5
waited and watched, with his mind made up, till he saw the men begin to square

up new stakes. . . .

—"The King of Mazy May" by Jack London

---

1 In the passage the word evidently means—
   A slowly
   B apparently
   C confusingly
   D questionably

2 In the passage the word cautiously means—
   A roughly
   B imaginatively
   C carefully
   D loudly

3 In the passage the word applying means—
   A submitting a request
   B snubbing
   C striving to bother
   D attempting to bribe

4 In the passage the word rapidly means—
   A incorrectly
   B slowly
   C quickly
   D carelessly

5 In the passage the word injustice means—
   A benefit
   B unconcern
   C distrust
   D unfairness

Reading Comprehension
Context Clues

Read the passage, and then answer the questions below it. Mark the letter of your answer on a bubble sheet if your teacher provides one; otherwise, circle the letter of the correct answer.

Robert Louis Stevenson was a <u>puzzle</u>. He grew up a <u>frail</u> boy in Scotland and

1   2

was <u>troubled</u> by poor health throughout his life. However, this sickly author wrote

3

stirring tales of adventure, like *Treasure Island*.

Tall and thin, with a storklike walk, Stevenson looked as if he could be <u>toppled</u>

4

by a gust of wind. Yet he was secretly tough and traveled all over the world.

Perhaps the puzzle of his own nature <u>prompted</u> him to write *The Strange Case*

5

of Dr. Jekyll and Mr. Hyde. This thriller, whose hero has a divided personality,

inspired several movies and a Broadway musical.

---

1 In the passage the word <u>puzzle</u> means—
  A difficult
  B mystery
  C complicated
  D a game

2 In the passage the word <u>frail</u> means—
  A weak
  B healthy
  C robust
  D proud

3 In the passage the word <u>troubled</u> means—
  A instructed
  B blessed
  C bothered
  D freed

4 In the passage the word <u>toppled</u> means—
  A knocked over
  B sickened
  C turned
  D irritated

5 In the passage the word <u>prompted</u> means—
  A forced
  B inspired
  C prevented
  D discouraged

Reading Comprehension

Context Clues

Read the passage, and then answer the questions below it. Mark the letter of your answer on a bubble sheet if your teacher provides one; otherwise, circle the letter of the correct answer.

The romance of it was almost unbearable on my first day as I trudged west
    1   2

along Lombard Street, then south along Gilmor, and east down Pratt Street with

the bundle of newspapers strapped to my hip. I imagined people pausing to

admire me as I performed this important work, spreading the news of the world,
3

the city, and the racetracks onto doorsteps, through mail slots, and under door

jambs. I had often gazed with envy at paperboys; to be one of them at last was
                                         4

happiness sublime.[1]

   . . . Deems announced a competition with mouth-watering prizes for the
                                   5

newsboys who got the most new subscribers.

1. sublime, *adj.*: Majestic; causing awe

—"Hard as Nails" by Russell Baker

---

1 In the passage the word
romance means—
  A pain
  B pressure
  C embarrassment
  D excitement

2 In the passage the word trudged
means—
  A glided
  B walked heavily
  C sobbed
  D skipped lightly

3 In the passage the word admire
means—
  A adore
  B greet
  C marvel at
  D regard with patience

4 In the passage the word envy
means—
  A hatred
  B jealousy
  C anger
  D warmth

5 In the passage the word
competition means—
  A contest
  B game
  C activity
  D hobby

Reading Comprehension
Recognize Facts and Details

Read the passage, and then answer the questions below it. Mark the letter of your answer on a bubble sheet if your teacher provides one; otherwise, circle the letter of the correct answer.

We shy persons need to write a letter now and then, or else we'll dry up and blow away. It's true. And I speak as one who loves to reach for the phone, dial the number, and talk. I say, "Big Bopper here—what's shakin', babes?" The telephone is to shyness what Hawaii is to February, it's a way out of the woods, *and yet:* a letter is better. . . .

The first step in writing letters is to get over the guilt of *not* writing. You don't "owe" anybody a letter. Letters are a gift. The burning shame you feel when you see unanswered mail makes it harder to pick up a pen and makes for a cheerless letter when you finally do. *I feel bad about not writing, but I've been so busy,* etc. Skip this.

—"How to Write a Letter" by Garrison Keillor

---

1 For whom is it especially important to write letters?
  A Lonely people
  B People who live alone
  C Shy people
  D People without pets

2 The narrator—
  A is afraid to talk on the phone
  B loves to talk on the phone
  C feels angry when on the phone
  D feels sad when on the phone

3 For shy people telephones are—
  A a way to be less shy
  B a way they can keep being shy
  C the best way to keep in touch with friends
  D a kind of vacation

4 The first step in writing a letter is—
  A to explain that you've been busy
  B to say why you have not written
  C to clean up your desk
  D to get over the guilt of not writing

5 The shame you feel when you see unanswered mail—
  A is a reasonable way to feel
  B is a stupid way to feel
  C is what keeps you from writing
  D is what makes you use the phone

6 Writing a letter is like—
  A paying a debt
  B sending an invitation
  C offering a kiss
  D giving a gift

Reading Comprehension
Recognize Facts and Details

Read the passage, and then answer the questions below it. Mark the letter of your answer on a bubble sheet if your teacher provides one; otherwise, circle the letter of the correct answer.

The morning after my teacher came she led me into her room and gave me a doll. The little blind children at the Perkins Institution had sent it and Laura Bridgman had dressed it; but I did not know this until afterward. When I had played with it a little while, Miss Sullivan slowly spelled into my hand the word "d-o-l-l." I was at once interested in this finger play and tried to imitate it. When I finally succeeded in making the letters correctly; I was flushed with childish pleasure and pride. Running downstairs to my mother I held up my hand and made the letters for doll. I did not know that I was spelling a word or even that words existed; I was simply making my fingers go in monkey-like imitation.

—"Water" by Helen Keller

---

1 The narrator receives a doll—
   A first thing in the morning
   B right after her teacher left
   C the morning after her teacher came
   D when the other children were gone

2 The lesson begins—
   A at once
   B after she plays with the doll
   C before she can undress the doll
   D after the teacher gives directions

3 The narrator first tries to make the letters because—
   A she likes how it feels
   B she wants to talk
   C her parents will be proud
   D the finger play interests her

4 She is able to make the letters—
   A after trying several times
   B right away
   C only to her mother
   D when she holds the doll

5 She is "flushed with childish pleasure and pride" because—
   A she knows the doll's name
   B she is able to make the letters
   C she has learned to spell
   D she has a new doll

Reading Comprehension
Recognize Facts and Details

Read the passage, and then answer the questions below it. Mark the letter of your answer on a bubble sheet if your teacher provides one; otherwise, circle the letter of the correct answer.

There are rivers
that I know,
born of ice
and melting snow,
with rapids,
swift to roar,
with no farms
along their shore,
with no cattle
come to drink
at a staid[1]
and welcoming brink,
with no millwheel,
ever turning,
in that cold
relentless[2] churning.

Only deer
and bear and mink
at those shallows
come to drink,
only paddles,
swift and light,
flick that current
in their flight.
I have felt
my heart beat high,
watching
with exultant[3] eye,
those pure rivers
which have known
no will, no purpose
but their own.

1. staid, *adj.*: Calm, steady   2. relentless, *adj.*: Never-ending   3. exultant, *adj.*: Joyful

—"Wilderness Rivers" by Elizabeth Coatsworth

---

1 The best word to describe the river as it is described in the poem is—
A useful
B wild
C cold
D busy

2 No cattle come to drink at the river because—
A it is too cold
B there are no farms near it
C they are afraid of the bears
D they cannot get by the fences

3 The current of the river is—
A slow and peaceful
B clogged with ice
C fast and constant
D too rough for a millwheel

4 When the poet looks at rivers such as this one she feels—
A lonely
B angry
C proud
D joyful

5 The poet is most impressed by rivers such as this one because—
A they serve no purpose but their own
B they provide shelter for wild animals
C they are not polluted
D no one else knows about them

Reading Comprehension
Recognize Facts and Details

Read the passage, and then answer the questions below it. Mark the letter of your answer on a bubble sheet if your teacher provides one; otherwise, circle the letter of the correct answer.

. . . Noah was a good man. God and he were like friends. So God said to his friend, "Noah! The world has become a sordid, wicked place and I'm sorry I ever made it. I will wash it clean with a flood. So build a wooden ship—an ark . . . Build it three stories high, and take aboard your wife and three sons—oh, and their wives, too. Then find every kind of animal—a male and a female of every bird and beast—and load them on, too. . . . Don't forget provisions, mind! Plenty of food for yourselves and the animals!"

Noah did exactly as he was told, whether or not his neighbors jeered and pointed and called him a madman, pelting him with pebbles and abuse. He set about building—right there, in the middle of dry land. He and his family went aboard, but it was seven days more before the rain came.

Then, in out of the wet came all the birds and beasts on Earth—two by two, as lightning tore the heavens open like a ripsaw and let fall the rains in torrents.

The rising water shifted, then lifted the ark . . . Standing at the rail, Noah saw the fields silvered over, his mud house crumbling, whole cities filled to the brim with water, and everyone—every wicked living soul—run, wade, swim, scream, then sink in the mud-brown Flood. Noah, his family, his zoo—and God—watched it happen.

When, after forty days and forty nights, the rain finally stopped, water masked the face of the Earth. . . . The ark ran aground on the peak of Mount Ararat.

—"The Great Flood" retold by Geraldine McCaughrean

---

1 What did God ask his friend Noah to do?
   A Cleanse the world with a flood
   B Sail on the ocean
   C Bring only enough provisions for the people on board
   D Build an ark

2 How did Noah respond to God's request?
   A Hesitantly
   B Obediently
   C Reluctantly
   D Anxiously

3 How did Noah's neighbors react to him building a boat?
   A They thought Noah was crazy.
   B They helped Noah build the boat.
   C They were able to help Noah with his questions.
   D They didn't know Noah was building a boat.

4 According to this story, how many people were aboard the ark?
   A Five
   B Six
   C Seven
   D Eight

Reading Comprehension
Recognize Facts and Details

Read the passage, and then answer the questions below it. Mark the letter of your answer on a bubble sheet if your teacher provides one; otherwise, circle the letter of the correct answer.

At Hanukkah[1] time the road from the village to the town is usually covered with snow, but this year the winter had been a mild one. Hanukkah had almost come, yet little snow had fallen. The sun shone most of the time. The peasants complained that because of the dry weather there would be a poor harvest of winter grain. New grass sprouted, and the peasants sent their cattle out to pasture.

For Reuven the furrier it was a bad year, and after long hesitation he decided to sell Zlateh the goat. She was old and gave little milk. Feivel the town butcher had offered eight gulden[2] for her. Such a sum would buy Hanukkah candles, potatoes and oil for pancakes, gifts for the children, and other holiday necessaries for the house. Reuven told his oldest boy Aaron to take the goat to town.

1. Hanukkah, *n.*: Jewish festival celebrated for eight days in early winter. Hanukkah is also called the "festival of lights" because a candle is lit on each of the eight days

2. gulden, *n.*: Unit of money

—"Zlateh the Goat" by Issac Bashevis Singer

1 The boy who is to sell the goat is named—
  A Aaron
  B Reuven
  C Zlateh
  D Feivel

2 There will be a poor harvest because—
  A the winter has been so harsh
  B there has been too much snow
  C there has not been enough snow
  D the summer has been too hot

3 The peasants send their cattle out to pasture because—
  A they have run out of grain
  B the grass has sprouted
  C they do not have water for the cows
  D the sun shines most of the time

4 The furrier decides to sell the goat—
  A as soon as the weather clears
  B so he can harvest the winter grain
  C because she has become mean
  D after delaying a long time

5 The goat will be sold to—
  A a wealthier family
  B the butcher
  C new neighbors
  D his eldest son

6 The goat will be sold—
  A for thirty dollars
  B for less than she is worth
  C in the town
  D at the fair

Reading Comprehension

Recognize Facts and Details

Read the passage, and then answer the questions below it. Mark the letter of your answer on a bubble sheet if your teacher provides one; otherwise, circle the letter of the correct answer.

If you sit down at set of sun
And count the acts that you have done,
    And counting, find
One self-denying deed, one word
That eased[1] the heart of him who heard,
    One glance most kind
That fell like sunshine where it went—
Then you may count that day well spent.

But if, through all the livelong day,
You have cheered no heart, by yea or nay—
    If, through it all
You have nothing done that you can trace
That brought the sunshine to one face—
    No act most small
That helped some soul and nothing cost—
Then count that day as worse than lost.

1. eased, v.: Comforted; freed from pain or worry

—"Count That Day Lost" by George Eliot

---

1 The poem proposes thinking of your actions—
   A at the beginning of the day
   B throughout the day
   C each time you act
   D at the end of the day

2 If your day is to be worthwhile you must—
   A always be aware of others
   B do one selfless thing for someone
   C speak kindly to strangers
   D comfort people in trouble

3 One deed that can make your day well spent is—
   A a big smile
   B bright eyes
   C a kind glance
   D a good thought

4 In this poem sunshine is compared to—
   A unselfishness
   B happiness
   C freedom
   D gratitude

5 According to the poem, you should make someone happy—
   A whenever you can
   B at least once a day
   C without thinking about it
   D unless you are ill

6 Your day is worse than lost if—
   A you do not make one person happier
   B you say one unkind word
   C you do not help everyone you see
   D you do not make a new friend

Reading Comprehension
Recognize Facts and Details

Read the passage, and then answer the questions below it. Mark the letter of your answer on a bubble sheet if your teacher provides one; otherwise, circle the letter of the correct answer.

To the best of my knowledge, there's never been a regulation[1] that forbids one to keep pets in a space station. No one ever thought it was necessary—and even had such a rule existed, I am quite certain that Sven Olson would have ignored it.

With a name like that, you will picture Sven at once as a six-foot-six Nordic giant, built like a bull and with a voice to match. Had this been so, his chances of getting a job in space would have been very slim. Actually he was a wiry little fellow, like most of the early spacers, and managed to qualify easily for the 150-pound bonus that kept so many of us on a reducing diet.

Sven was one of our best construction men, and excelled at the tricky and specialized work of collecting assorted girders as they floated around in free fall, making them do the slow-motion, three dimensional ballet that would get them into their right positions, and fusing[2] the pieces together when they were precisely dovetailed into the intended pattern: it was a skilled and difficult job . . .

1. regulation, n.: Rule
2. fusing, v.: Joining permanently

—"Feathered Friend" by Arthur C. Clarke

---

1 As far as the narrator knows, pets in space stations—
   A have never been allowed
   B have never been regulated
   C are a good idea
   D are very common

2 The narrator thinks Sven—
   A would ignore some rules
   B is a very nice person
   C would make a good officer
   D is a Nordic giant

3 The narrator says Sven's name will make people think—
   A Sven disobeys rules
   B Sven likes to fight
   C Sven is very tall
   D Sven shouts a good deal

4 Physically, Sven is—
   A blond
   B broad shouldered
   C fat, but strong
   D lean

5 Sven and his fellow workers are compared to—
   A deep sea divers
   B dancers
   C circus performers
   D astronauts

6 The narrator calls Sven's work—
   A painful
   B thankless
   C specialized
   D beautiful

Reading Comprehension

Identify the Main Idea;
Recognize Facts and Details

Read the passage, and then answer the questions below it. Mark the letter of your answer on a bubble sheet if your teacher provides one; otherwise, circle the letter of the correct answer.

When Nonno Frankie arrived on Saturday morning, he found me sitting in the apple tree alone. Mom had told him it was O.K. to walk around the whole yard now, as long as he didn't do any diggings or mutilations other than weed-pulling on her side. I was expecting him to notice right off the bat that I was white with fear, but instead he stood looking at the carvings Jennifer and I had made in the trunk of the tree. I thought he was just intensely curious about what "ESCAPE! PAUL & JENNIFER!" meant. Of course, the twins, being such copycats, had already added their names so the full carving away of the bark now read, "ESCAPE! PAUL & JENNIFER! & NICKY & JOEY!" And the letters circled halfway around the tree.

—"The Pigman & Me" by Paul Zindel

---

1 What is the main idea of this passage?
  A Nonno Frankie likes to walk in the yard.
  B The narrator is sitting alone in the apple tree.
  C Nonno Frankie does not notice the narrator's fear.
  D The narrator's mother does not like Nonno Frankie.

2 The narrator assumes Nonno Frankie does not notice his feelings because—
  A the narrator cannot see Nonno Frankie
  B Nonno Frankie is looking at the tree
  C Nonno Frankie does not speak to him
  D the twins are such copycats

3 Nonno Frankie may walk around the yard if—
  A he asks permission first
  B he does not dig in it
  C he scolds the narrator for digging
  D he pulls weeds for the narrator's mother

4 The twins are copycats because—
  A they climb the tree
  B they follow Nonno Frankie in the yard
  C they always imitate Nonno Frankie
  D they add their names on the tree

5 The emotion most central to this passage is—
  A the narrator's fear
  B Nonno Frankie's boredom
  C the twin's selfishness
  D Jennifer's jealousy

Reading Comprehension

Identify the Main Idea;
Recognize Facts and Details

Read the passage, and then answer the questions below it. Mark the letter of your answer on a bubble sheet if your teacher provides one; otherwise, circle the letter of the correct answer.

The ascent sharply steepened and the stone rose with him as Norman climbed. What looked like a smooth path from the prairie floor was rough rocky terrain. The trail spiraled up a sharp incline and Norman had to detour around fallen rocks. He paused to rest about halfway up and then saw how sharply the overhanging ledge of the butte protruded. Getting to the top of it was going to be a difficult struggle. He climbed on. His foot slipped and his ankle twisted painfully. Small pebbles bounced down the slope and he saw a rattlesnake slither out of the way. He tightly clutched the willow branch and leaned panting against the butte. He sighed with relief as the snake crawled out of sight. He wiggled his foot until the pain left his ankle. Then he started to trudge up the incline again.

—"Thunder Butte" by Virginia Driving Hawk Sneve

---

1 What is the main idea of this passage?
   A Norman is not an experienced climber.
   B Norman escaped a rattlesnake.
   C Norman is having a hard time climbing.
   D Norman will not be able to finish his climb.

2 Having begun his climb, Norman finds—
   A the terrain is rougher than he thought
   B he has begun much too early
   C he has no water
   D he will have to rest halfway up

3 Norman's main goal is—
   A avoiding rattlesnakes
   B finishing before sundown
   C getting to the top
   D not getting hurt

4 When Norman stops to rest,—
   A he twists his ankle
   B he is bitten by a snake
   C he wishes he had not started to climb
   D he sees how hard the climb is

5 Norman uses the willow branch—
   A to frighten the snake
   B to keep his balance
   C to mark his trail
   D to get some shade

6 Norman's twisted ankle—
   A will keep him from climbing on
   B does not really hurt
   C is painful for a short time
   D makes him bounce down the slope

Reading Comprehension:

Identify the Main Idea;
Recognize Facts and Details

Read the passage, and then answer the questions below it. Mark the letter of your answer on a bubble sheet if your teacher provides one; otherwise, circle the letter of the correct answer.

I recall the occasion of my first appearance. San Francisco knew me then only as a reporter, and I was to make my bow to San Francisco as a lecturer. I knew that nothing short of compulsion would get me to the theater. So I bound myself by a hard-and-fast contract so that I could not escape. I got to the theater forty-five minutes before the hour set for the lecture. My knees were shaking so that I didn't know whether I could stand up. If there is an awful, horrible malady in the world, it is stage fright—and seasickness. They are a pair. I had stage fright then for the first and last time. I was only seasick once, too. It was on a little ship on which there were two hundred other passengers. I—was—sick. I was so sick that there wasn't any left for those other two hundred passengers.

—"Stage Fright" by Mark Twain

---

1 What is the main point of this passage?
A To explain what stage fright is
B To tell why the writer got to the theater early
C To compare stage fright and seasickness
D To describe how the writer's stage fright felt

2 The narrator gets a strict contract so that—
A he will get plenty of money for his pain
B the audience cannot change its mind
C he did not want to go to San Francisco
D he will be forced to show up at the theater

3 Before his first appearance, he was known as a—
A writer
B television actor
C reporter
D coward

4 After this first appearance, his stage fright—
A worsened
B made him feel seasick
C left him unable to stand
D went away

5 Stage fright and seasickness "are a pair" because—
A seasickness causes stage fright
B stage fright causes seasickness
C both are horrible maladies
D both happen in front of people

6 The writer has contracted with the theater to—
A deliver a lecture
B act in a play
C sing a song
D tell a story

Reading Comprehension:

Identify the Main Idea;
Recognize Facts and Details

Read the passage, and then answer the questions below it. Mark the letter of your answer on a bubble sheet if your teacher provides one; otherwise, circle the letter of the correct answer.

Dear Richard,

Don't invite me to your birthday party because I'm not coming. And give back the Disneyland sweatshirt I said you could wear. If I'm not good enough to play on your team, I'm not good enough to be friends with.

Your former friend,

Janet

P.S. I hope when you go to the dentist he finds 20 cavities.

Dear Janet,

Here is your stupid Disneyland sweatshirt, if that's how you're going to be. I want my comic books now—finished or not. No girl has ever played on the Mapes Street baseball team, and as long as I'm captain, no girl ever will.

Your former friend,

Richard

P.S. I hope when you go for your checkup you need a tetanus shot.

—"The Southpaw" by Judith Viorst

---

1 What is the main point of the first letter?

A For Janet to tell Richard she will not come to his party

B For Janet to get her sweatshirt back

C For Janet to insult Richard

D For Janet to tell Richard that not allowing her to play on his team will end their friendship

2 What is the main point of the second letter?

A For Richard to get his comic books back

B For Richard to tell Janet he will not change his mind

C For Richard to insult Janet

D For Richard to tell Janet he hates the sweatshirt

3 Janet does not want to be Richard's friend because—

A he will not let her play on his team

B she feels she is not good enough

C he will not return her sweatshirt

D he did not invite her to his party

4 Richard does not want Janet on the team because—

A she is a poor player

B she never shows up for practice

C she is a girl

D she is a better player than he is

Reading Comprehension:

Identify the Main Idea;
Recognize Facts and Details

Read the passage, and then answer the questions below it. Mark the letter of your answer on a bubble sheet if your teacher provides one; otherwise, circle the letter of the correct answer.

Said Orville Wright to Wilbur Wright,
"These birds are very trying.
I'm sick of hearing them cheep-cheep
About the fun of flying.
A bird has feathers, it is true.
That much I freely grant.
But, must that stop us, W?"
Said Wilbur Wright, "It shan't."

And so they built a glider, first,
And then they built another.
—There never were two brothers more
Devoted to each other.
They ran a dusty little shop
For bicycle-repairing,
And bought each other soda-pop
and praised each other's daring.

—"Wilbur Wright and Orville Wright" by Rosemary and Stephen Vincent Benét

---

1 What is the main point of the first stanza?
   A The Wright brothers are very observant.
   B The birds make fun of the Wright brothers.
   C The Wright brothers will fly without feathers.
   D Orville talks to the birds.

2 What is the main point of the second stanza?
   A Orville and Wilbur get along well.
   B Orville and Wilbur work hard.
   C Orville and Wilbur repair bicycles.
   D Orville and Wilbur built a glider.

3 Orville assumes that birds—
   A talk too much
   B are proud of their feathers
   C have fun flying
   D have to try hard to talk

4 What the brothers want to do most is—
   A drink soda
   B repair bicycles
   C talk to birds
   D fly

5 In order to fly, the brothers—
   A praised each other for being daring
   B gathered feathers
   C bought soda pop
   D built a glider

6 According to the poem, the brothers can best be described as—
   A dusty
   B eager
   C silly
   D tired

Reading Comprehension
Perceive Cause and Effect

Read the passage, and then answer the questions below it. Mark the letter of your answer on a bubble sheet if your teacher provides one; otherwise, circle the letter of the correct answer.

Arithmetic tells you how many you lose or win if you know how many you had
   before you lost or won.
Arithmetic is seven eleven all good children go to heaven—or five six bundle of
   sticks.
Arithmetic is numbers you squeeze from your head to your hand to your pencil to
   your paper till you get the answer.
Arithmetic is where the answer is right and everything is nice and you can look out
   of the window and see the blue sky—or the answer is wrong and you have to
   start all over and try again and see how it comes out this time.
If you take a number and double it and double it again and then double it a few
   more times, the number gets bigger and bigger and goes higher and higher and
   only arithmetic can tell you what the number is when you decide to quit doubling.

—"Arithmetic" by Carl Sandburg

---

1 Arithmetic tells you how many you win or lose only if—
  A you win more than you lose
  B you lose more than you win
  C you squeeze the answer to your paper
  D you know how many you started with

2 To solve an arithmetic problem you must use—
  A your head first
  B your hand first
  C your pencil first
  D your paper first

3 You can look out of the window and see the blue sky—
  A when you get a right answer in arithmetic
  B if you really like arithmetic
  C whenever you do arithmetic
  D when you make rhymes with arithmetic

4 When the answer to an arithmetic problem is wrong—
  A you can still make rhymes with numbers
  B you can look out the window at the blue sky
  C you have to stay after school
  D you have to start all over

5 If you take a number, double it, and double it again—
  A you are using advanced mathematics
  B only arithmetic can tell you your answer
  C the number will be too high to remember
  D everything will be nice

Reading Comprehension
Perceive Cause and Effect

Read the passage, and then answer the questions below it. Mark the letter of your answer on a bubble sheet if your teacher provides one; otherwise, circle the letter of the correct answer.

> When his father died, the peasant Kwan Ming was forced to sell his little plot of paddy and the old family house to pay for the burial. After the funeral, Kwan Ming looked around at the banana trees surrounding his village, and saw that he had nothing left to his name—not even one chipped roof tile. He had just enough money to buy a steamship ticket to the New World, where he had heard jobs were plentiful.
>
> "I can start a new life there," he told his mother. "I will send money home."
>
> The voyage lasted six weeks, over rocky waves and through screaming storms. Kwan Ming huddled together with hundreds of other Chinese deep in the ship's hold. There he became fast friends with Chew Lap, Tam Yim and Wong Foon— men from neighboring villages.
>
> —"The Friends of Kwan Ming" by Paul Yee

1 Why did Kwan Ming sell the paddy and house after his father died?
   A This was the custom in his land.
   B Kwan Ming did not want to be reminded of his father.
   C Kwan Ming's mother wanted to move to a new house.
   (D) The family had no money for the father's burial.

[handwritten left margin: So they sold the House]

2 Why did Kwan Ming have nothing left to his name after the funeral?
   (A) He had given everything away.
   B He had spent his money on a steamship ticket.
   C He had sold all of his property.
   D He had cut down his father's banana trees.

[handwritten left margin: No money to pay for the Burial]

[handwritten: (fiction) or nonfiction]

[handwritten: Authers purpas infertune]

3 What caused Kwan Ming to leave his homeland?
   A He did not get along with his mother.
   B He lost his old way of life when he sold the property.
   C The banana trees reminded him of his father.
   D He could not fix the chipped tile in his roof.

[handwritten right margin: No House & No Job]

4 Kwan Ming decided to go to the New World because—
   A he thought that was where his father wanted him to go
   B he thought his mother wanted him to go
   (C) he thought he could find a job
   D he thought he could make new friends

[handwritten right margin: Jobs, frenzs and money]

5 Kwan Ming's journey to the new world was—
   (A) rough and stormy
   B peaceful and calm
   C six months long
   D spent with old friends

[handwritten: in text]

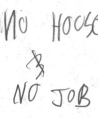
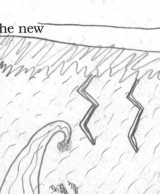

Name _____ Class _____ Date _____

Reading Comprehension
Perceive Cause and Effect

Read the passage, and then answer the questions below it. Mark the letter of your answer on a bubble sheet if your teacher provides one; otherwise, circle the letter of the correct answer.

Now the fisherman was also sad that they had no child. But he kept his sorrow to himself so that his wife would not know his grief and thus double her own. Indeed, he would leave the hut each morning with a breath of song and return each night with a whistle on his lips. His nets were full but his heart was empty, yet he never told his wife.

One sunny day, when the beach was a tan thread spun between sea and plain, the fisherman as usual went down to his boat. But this day he found a small grey seal stranded on the sandbar, crying for its own.

—"Greyling" by Jane Yolen

1 The fisherman was sad because—
  A he had no father
  B his wife had no mother
  C the seal had no parents
  D he and his wife had no child

2 The fisherman acted cheerfully because—
  A he didn't want to make his wife sad too
  B he knew one day they would have a child
  C he loved to fish
  D he had stopped longing for a child

3 The fisherman went down to his boat—
  A to hide from his wife
  B because he did so most everyday
  C to meet the seal
  D because he was sad

4 The fisherman left the house singing and returned whistling because—
  A he was happy
  B he was trying to appear happy
  C he was sad
  D he was trying to appear sad

5 The fisherman's heart was empty because—
  A he did not love his wife
  B his nets were empty
  C he did not love children
  D he had no child to love

6 The seal's feelings can best be described as—
  A excited
  B hungry
  C lonely
  D angry

27

Reading Comprehension
Perceive Cause and Effect

Read the passage, and then answer the questions below it. Mark the letter of your answer on a bubble sheet if your teacher provides one; otherwise, circle the letter of the correct answer.

Afoot and light-hearted, I take to the open road,
Healthy, free, the world before me,
The long brown path before me, leading wherever I choose.

Henceforth I ask not good-fortune, I myself am good-fortune,
Henceforth I whimper no more, postpone no more, need nothing,
Done with indoor complaints, libraries, querulous criticisms,
Strong and content, I travel the open road.

—"The Open Road" by Walt Whitman

---

1 The author might feel light-hearted because—
 A he is able to walk down the street
 B he does not need to make any choices
 C he has many opportunities from which to choose
 D someone else had already made all his decisions for him

2 The first thing the author does is—
 A stop whimpering
 B visit a library
 C stop complaining
 D go on a journey

3 The long brown path leads wherever the author chooses because—
 A he has given himself the freedom to wander
 B his journey is already planned
 C he is too weak to make decisions
 D he is going to wait before making any decisions

4 The author has decided not to ask for good-fortune anymore because—
 A he knows it is useless to ask
 B he does not want any good-fortune
 C he still depends on others to make him happy
 D he is his own good-fortune

5 Why does the author find the open road so appealing?
 A He does not want to change his behavior.
 B He is tired of people who complain.
 C He wants to meet new people.
 D He is looking for new books to read.

6 The author sets out strong and content because—
 A he thinks he does not need anyone or anything
 B he feels sorry for other people
 C he feels sorry for himself
 D he is tired of being criticized

Name _____ Class _____ Date _____

Reading Comprehension
Perceive Cause and Effect

Read the passage, and then answer the questions below it. Mark the letter of your answer on a bubble sheet if your teacher provides one; otherwise, circle the letter of the correct answer.

It was 1945, and World War II had ended. Americans of all races had died for their country. Yet black men were still not allowed in the major leagues. . . .

Branch Rickey of the Brooklyn Dodgers thought that was wrong. He was the only team owner who believed blacks and whites should play together. Baseball, he felt, would become even more thrilling, and fans of all colors would swarm to his ballpark.

Rickey decided his team would be the first to integrate. There were plenty of brilliant Negro league players, but he knew the first black major leaguer would need much more than athletic ability. . . .

When Rickey met Jackie Robinson, he thought he'd found the right man. Robinson was 28 years old, and a superb athlete. In his first season in the Negro leagues, he hit .387. But just as importantly, he had great intelligence and sensitivity. Robinson was college-educated, and knew what joining the majors would mean for blacks. The grandson of a slave, he was proud of his race and wanted others to feel the same.

—"Jackie Robinson: Justice at Last" by Geoffrey C. Ward and Ken Burns

---

1 Black men probably did not play in the major leagues in 1945 because—
  A they were not good athletes
  B they were not interested in playing baseball
  C most of the owners believed in segregation
  D the fans did not want to see black players

2 Rickey decided to integrate his team because—
  A he wanted to get better players
  B he wanted his team to do what the other teams did
  C his team was the only one with no black players
  D he thought it was wrong that only white men were allowed to play

3 Why did Rickey think fans would swarm to integrated games?
  A He felt sure his fans were not racist.
  B There were more black fans than white fans.
  C They would want to see the players fight.
  D The quality of the games would be better.

4 Robinson thought joining the majors—
  A would get even for his grandfather
  B had nothing to do with race
  C would make people proud of his race
  D would be a mistake

Reading Comprehension
Draw Conclusions; Make Inferences

Read the passage, and then answer the questions below it. Mark the letter of your answer on a bubble sheet if your teacher provides one; otherwise, circle the letter of the correct answer.

Archaeological methods took a great step forward in the twentieth century, and various sciences were now joined together in investigations. Astronomy was one of these. . . .

Astronomy and archaeology had now confirmed each other. Stonehenge had not been built by the Druids, but a thousand years before their time. In 1950 this date was established in a third way, for charcoal dug from one of the Aubrey Holes confirmed it. Carbon 14 dating placed the construction at 1847 B.C., with a possible variation of 225 years.

So the cool, precise work of the scientists put an end to legends and superstitions. There could be no more talk of Druids at Stonehenge now. Nevertheless, the ancient structure was as mysterious as it had ever been. Whence had the great stones come? Why were they of two different kinds?

—"The Strange Geometry of Stonehenge" by Katherine B. Shippen

---

1 What can you conclude about archaeology in the twentieth century?
 A The methods were not advanced enough to answer any questions.
 B The methods changed a lot and became more useful.
 C The methods were based on legends and superstitions.
 D The methods were not helpful when used by themselves.

2 Information from scientific investigations can be used—
 A only to support ideas that are true
 B only to disprove ideas that are false
 C to support some ideas and disprove others
 D to create legends and superstitions

3 Using different areas of science to study the same problem—
 A has never been done
 B is always useful
 C is impossible to do
 D can be useful

4 The passage indicates that scientists try to—
 A solve problems logically and carefully
 B solve problems quickly
 C disprove ideas from other areas of science
 D prove that legends and superstitions are false

5 In the twentieth century,—
 A everyone believed that the Druids built Stonehenge
 B archaeologists proved that the Druids built Stonehenge
 C astronomers proved that the Druids built Stonehenge
 D some people believed the Druids built Stonehenge

Reading Comprehension

Make Inferences

Read the passage, and then answer the questions below it. Mark the letter of your answer on a bubble sheet if your teacher provides one; otherwise, circle the letter of the correct answer.

> . . . Margie always hated school, but now she hated it more than ever. The mechanical teacher had been giving her test after test in geography, and she had been doing worse and worse until her mother had shaken her head sorrowfully and sent for the county inspector.
>
> He was a round little man with a red face and a whole box of tools with dials and wires. He smiled at her and gave her an apple, then took the teacher apart. Margie had hoped he wouldn't know how to put it together again, but he knew how all right, and after an hour or so, there it was again, large and ugly, with a big screen on which all the lessons were shown and the questions were asked. That wasn't so bad. The part she hated most was the slot where she had to put homework and test papers. She always had to write them out in a punch code they made her learn when she was six years old, and the mechanical teacher calculated[1] the mark in no time.
>
> The inspector had smiled after he was finished and patted her head. He said to her mother, "It's not the little girl's fault, Mrs. Jones. I think the geography sector was geared a little too quick. Those things happen sometimes. I've slowed it up to an average ten-year level. Actually, the overall pattern of her progress is quite satisfactory." And he patted Margie's head again.
>
> 1. calculated, *v.*: Determined by using math
>
> —"The Fun They Had" by Isaac Asimov

1 Margie's mother was probably sad because—
  A she did not approve of Margie's teacher
  B she wanted Margie to do better in school
  C geography was not her favorite subject
  D she did not like the county inspector

2 Doing poorly in school probably made Margie—
  A dislike herself
  B dislike her mother
  C dislike the inspector
  D dislike the mechanical teacher

3 The inspector's job probably requires—
  A knowledge of geography
  B instructing parents
  C mechanical skills
  D grading tests

4 Overall, Margie is probably—
  A an excellent student
  B an above-average student
  C an average student
  D a poor student

5 What most likely caused Margie's poor performance in geography?
  A Her hatred of school
  B Her hatred of geography
  C Her mechanical teacher
  D Her disapproving mother

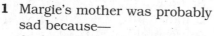

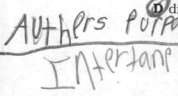

Reading Comprehension

Make Inferences

Read the passage, and then answer the questions below it. Mark the letter of your answer on a bubble sheet if your teacher provides one; otherwise, circle the letter of the correct answer.

In the spring of the year, in the spring of the year,
I walked the road beside my dear.
The trees were black where the bark was wet.
I see them yet, in the spring of the year.
He broke me a bough of the blossoming peach
That was out of the way and hard to reach.

In the fall of the year, in the fall of the year,
I walked the road beside my dear.
The rooks went up with a raucous trill.
I hear them still, in the fall of the year.
He laughed at all I dared to praise,
And broke my heart, in little ways.

—"The Spring and the Fall"
by Edna St. Vincent Millay

1 In this poem the speaker is talking about someone she—
 A pities
 B envies
 C distrusts
 D loves

2 How did the speaker probably feel in the spring?
 A Happy
 B Angry
 C Hurt
 D Confused

3 How did the speaker probably feel in the fall?
 A Happy
 B Angry
 C Hurt
 D Confused

4 In the spring of the year the man in the passage was—
 A caring
 B funny
 C indignant
 D scornful

5 In the fall of the year the man in the passage was—
 A caring
 B funny
 C indignant
 D scornful

6 What happened between the spring and the fall?
 A The speaker fell in love with the man.
 B The speaker fell out of love with the man.
 C The man fell in love with the speaker.
 D The man fell out of love with the speaker.

−4

Reading Comprehension
Make Inferences

Read the passage, and then answer the questions below it. Mark the letter of your answer on a bubble sheet if your teacher provides one; otherwise, circle the letter of the correct answer.

At 7:30 P.M., the radio room received three more warnings of ice about fifty miles ahead. One of them was from the steamer *Californian* reporting three large icebergs. Harold Bride took this message up to the bridge, and it was again politely received. Captain Smith was attending the dinner party being held for him when the warning was delivered. He never got to see it. Then, around 9:00 P.M., the captain excused himself and went up to the bridge. He and his officers talked about how difficult it was to spot icebergs on a calm, clear, moonless night like this with no wind to kick up white surf around them. Before going to bed, the captain ordered the lookouts to keep a sharp watch for ice.

—from *Exploring the Titanic* by Robert D. Ballard

They probly thought its. Just ice

1 The warning message was received politely because—
   A no one thought the ice was a real threat
   B no one wanted to admit he was scared
   C everyone knew the ice would melt quickly
   D Captain Smith was not on the bridge

Keep a veary sharp look out. He brout the messeg up to the Brid g

2 Captain Smith—
   A was very concerned about the ice
   B was mildly concerned about the ice
   C was not concerned about the ice
   D did not know about the ice

3 What was Harold Bride's position on the ship?
   A He was a passenger.
   B He was a waiter.
   C He worked in the radio room.
   D He worked on the bridge.

He never got to see it

4 Captain Smith never read the warning because—
   A his officers hid it from him
   B his officers did not tell him about it
   C his officers thought it was a joke
   D his officers wanted to run the ship

Because its the Titnic

5 The people in this passage were aboard a boat used for—
   A fishing
   B patrolling
   C carrying freight
   D carrying passengers

He probly wnted to go to Bed and

6 The captain talked about the difficulty of spotting an iceberg—
   A so he could hurry to bed
   B since the men seemed unconcerned
   C so there was no point in looking
   D so the watchers would be extra careful

Be lazy

no the one

Pictur   no pictur   time order

Reading Comprehension

Make Inferences

Read the passage, and then answer the questions below it. Mark the letter of your answer on a bubble sheet if your teacher provides one; otherwise, circle the letter of the correct answer.

> Orpheus loved a young woman named Eurydice, and when they were married, they looked forward to many years of happiness together. But soon after, Eurydice stepped on a poisonous snake and died.
>
> Orpheus roamed the earth, singing sad melodies to try to overcome his grief. But it was no use. He longed for Eurydice so deeply that he decided to follow her to the underworld. He said to himself, "No mortal has ever been there before, but I must try to bring back my beloved Eurydice. I will charm Persephone and Hades with my music and win Eurydice's release."
>
> —"Orpheus" by Alice Low

1 After Eurydice died, she—
   A came back to life
   B roamed the earth
   C married someone else
   D was trapped in the underworld

in text

2 Orpheus and Eurydice—
   A were forced to marry each other
   B were not married for long
   C were married late in life
   D were never separated

in text

3 Which description best fits Orpheus?
   A Mortal
   B God
   C Magician
   D Underworld creature

in text

4 Orpheus was probably known for his extraordinary—
   A luck
   B patience
   C music
   D energy

I Gues that he has magical music

5 The underworld is a place where—
   A people go when they are sad
   B people go when they die
   C people go when they are lonely
   D people go when they are tired

you can asoume that sence she dided

6 Persephone and Hades probably—
   A created the underworld
   B destroyed the underworld
   C ruled the underworld
   D left the underworld

I think this is Right

Fiction or non Fiction

Aurthers purpes Intertune

Reading Comprehension
Draw Conclusions; Make Inferences

Read the passage, and then answer the questions below it. Mark the letter of your answer on a bubble sheet if your teacher provides one; otherwise, circle the letter of the correct answer.

Suddenly, they heard a distant roar. The official looked up at the sky. "It sounds like thunder, but I don't see a cloud in the sky."

Breaker cupped his hands around his mouth to amplify his voice. "Get out," he shouted to his men. "Get out. The river must have broken our dam."

His men slipped and slid on the muddy riverbed, but they all managed to scramble out just as a wall of water rolled down the gorge. The river swept around the two piers, pulling and tugging at the stones.

—"Breaker's Bridge" by Laurence Yep

---

1 What caused the sound the official heard?
- **A** A crowd roaring in the distance
- **B** Water pouring over the dam
- **C** Thunder crashing in the distance
- **D** Stones being pulled from the piers

(handwritten: in Text)

2 Breaker yelled to the men in the riverbed because they were—
- **A** ruining his project
- **B** ignoring the official
- **C** stuck in the mud
- **D** in the path of the water

(handwritten: makes the most sence out of all of them)

3 One can conclude that the riverbed—
- **A** had been dry for a long time
- **B** had recently been covered with water
- **C** was very wide with steep sides
- **D** had always been a dangerous place to work

(handwritten: If it is muddy then their Has to be water on it rencely)

4 The men in the riverbed were probably—
- **A** looking for the dam
- **B** hiding from Breaker
- **C** working on the piers
- **D** building the dam

(handwritten: "Distant Roar")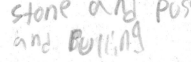

5 One can conclude that the piers were—
- **A** right below the dam
- **B** right above the dam
- **C** within sight of the dam
- **D** out of sight of the dam

(handwritten: in text)

6 One can conclude that the two piers were made of—
- **A** stone
- **B** wood
- **C** cement
- **D** metal

(handwritten: it talks about stone and pushi and pulling)

(handwritten: Authers purpos Intertane)

(handwritten: Fiction or non fiction)

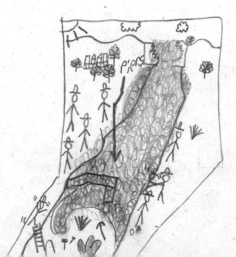

Reading Comprehension
Make Inferences

Read the passage, and then answer the questions below it. Mark the letter
of your answer on a bubble sheet if your teacher provides one; otherwise,
circle the letter of the correct answer.

Someone came knocking
　　At my wee, small door;
Someone came knocking,
　　I'm sure—sure—sure;
I listened, I opened,
　　I looked to left and right,
But nought there was a-stirring
　　In the still, dark night;
Only the busy beetle
　　Tap-tapping in the wall,
Only from the forest
　　The screech owl's call,
Only the cricket whistling
　　While the dewdrops fall,
So I know not who came knocking,
　　At all, at all, at all.

—"Someone" by Walter de la Mare

---

1 The speaker in this passage
　 lives—
　 A in a city
　 B in a town
　 C in the country
　 D by the beach

2 The night described in this
　 passage is—
　 A windy
　 B rainy
　 C snowy
　 D calm

3 Which word best describes the
　 speaker after the first knock is
　 heard?
　 A Curious
　 B Nervous
　 C Frightened
　 D Uneasy

4 The sounds the speaker heard
　 after the knocking were—
　 A sounds that he had never
　　 heard before
　 B sounds that he could not
　　 identify
　 C sounds that he knew well
　 D sounds that startled him

5 The speaker finally decided
　 that—
　 A no one had knocked upon
　　 his door
　 B the beetle had knocked upon
　　 his door
　 C the screech owl had flown into
　　 his door
　 D he would never know who had
　　 knocked on his door

Reading Comprehension
Draw Conclusions; Make Inferences

Read the passage, and then answer the questions below it. Mark the letter of your answer on a bubble sheet if your teacher provides one; otherwise, circle the letter of the correct answer.

> For the first time they began to understand the truth about this arm of Loch Ness. Underwater, along both sides of the bay, were deep hidden ravines, rocky canyons and caves, dark recesses far below the surface. This excited the research team. The hiding places made the whole story of Nessie more believable. Nessie, it was agreed, could cruise about down there among those dark caves without sending a ripple to the surface.
>
> This is also the area in which one earlier investigator heard strange underwater sounds the year before, tapping sounds that no biologist has yet been able to successfully identify.
>
> —"The Loch Ness Monster" by George Laycock

1 One can conclude that Loch Ness is—
A a swimming hole
B a pond
C a lake
D an ocean

2 The researchers were interested in—
A learning if Nessie could live in Loch Ness
B discovering new caves in Loch Ness
C measuring the depth of Loch Ness
D drawing a map of Loch Ness

3 The researchers were excited because—
A they solved the mystery of Loch Ness
B they found Nessie in Loch Ness
C they understood all about Loch Ness
D they found hidden features in Loch Ness

4 The story of Nessie is probably based on—
A dreams
B legends
C tricks
D facts

5 The research team probably studied Loch Ness for—
A many days
B one day
C many hours
D one hour

6 Nessie could move about without making ripples because—
A the water was so thick
B the water was so smooth
C the water was so dark
D the water was so deep

Reading Comprehension
Describe Plot and Character

Read the passage, and then answer the questions below it. Mark the letter of your answer on a bubble sheet if your teacher provides one; otherwise, circle the letter of the correct answer.

There was once a king whose kingdom was plagued[1] by a dragon. The king did not know which way to turn. The king's knights were all cowards who hid under their beds whenever the dragon came in sight, so they were of no use to the king at all. . . .

Every time there was a full moon the dragon came out of his lair and ravaged[2] the countryside. . . .

"That," said the king in a fury, "is enough!" And he called a meeting of everyone in the kingdom. . . .

"Ladies and gentlemen," said the king when everyone was present, "I've put up with that dragon as long as I can. He has got to be stopped."

All the people whispered amongst themselves, and the king smiled, pleased with the impression he had made.

But the wise cobbler said gloomily, "It's all very well to talk about it—but how are you going to do it?"

And now all the people smiled and winked as if to say, "Well, King, he's got you there!"

The king frowned.

1. plagued, v.: Tormented
2. ravaged, v.: Violently destroyed; ruined

—"Dragon, Dragon" by John Gardner

1 Which of the following best describes the king's feelings toward the dragon?
   A Fear
   B Frustration
   C Sorrow
   D Disgust

2 What character trait does the king show when speaking to the crowd?
   A Wisdom
   B Weakness
   C Fear
   D Pride

3 Which of the following best describes how the king felt after the cobbler spoke?
   A Proud
   B Excited
   C Embarrassed
   D Unhappy

4 What was the king's motive for calling together all the people?
   A He wanted to seem powerful.
   B He wanted to devise a plan to get rid of the dragon.
   C He wanted to talk to the cobbler.
   D He simply wanted to make a speech.

Reading Comprehension
Describe Plot and Character

Read the passage, and then answer the questions below it. Mark the letter of your answer on a bubble sheet if your teacher provides one; otherwise, circle the letter of the correct answer.

> I know total-total that if I had my own bike, the Wheels-and-Brake Boys wouldn't treat me like that. I'd just ride away with them, wouldn't I?
>
> Over and over I told my mum I wanted a bike. Over and over she looked at me as if I was crazy. "Becky, d'you think you're a boy? Eh? D'you think you're a boy? In any case, where's the money to come from? Eh?"
>
> Of course I know I'm not a boy. Of course I know I'm not crazy. Of course I know all that's no reason why I can't have a bike. No reason! As soon as I get indoors I'll just have to ask again—ask Mum once more.
>
> —"Becky and the Wheels-and-Brake Boys" by James Berry

1 The main conflict in the passage is between—
 A Becky and the boys
 B Becky and her mum
 C girls and boys
 D Becky and herself

2 What is Becky's motive for wanting a bike?
 A Greed
 B Jealousy
 C Anger
 D Acceptance

3 Which of the following best describes Becky's mum's feelings about Becky wanting a bike?
 A Frustrated
 B Approving
 C Indifferent
 D Excited

4 Which of the following best describes Becky's mum's reason for not getting Becky a bike?
 A Becky's mum can be mean sometimes.
 B She thinks bikes are for boys.
 C She does not have enough money to buy a bike.
 D She is frustrated with Becky.

5 Which character trait best describes Becky's strategy for getting a bike?
 A "Wait and see"
 B Persistent
 C Sneaky
 D Reasonable

6 What was Becky's main problem in this passage?
 A The boys will not let her join in their group.
 B She wants to have her own bike.
 C Her mum thinks bikes are only for boys.
 D They do not have enough money for a bike.

Picture

Fiction or non fiction

Authers purpas
Infertone

Reading Comprehension

Describe Character, Setting, and Mood

Read the passage, and then answer the questions below it. Mark the letter of your answer on a bubble sheet if your teacher provides one; otherwise, circle the letter of the correct answer.

It was dusk when the wagon drew away from the station. To the right of the surveyor stretched the dark, frozen plain—broad and endless. Try to cross it and you'll come to the end of the world. On the horizon, where the plain merged with the sky and disappeared, the autumn sun was lazily sinking in the mist. To the left of the road, in the darkening space, loomed oddly shaped mounds, and it was hard to tell whether they were last year's haystacks or the huts of a village. What there was ahead of them the surveyor could not tell because his field of vision was completely obstructed by the massive back of the driver. It was still, cold, frosty.

—"Overdoing It" by Anton Chekhov

---

1 In what season of the year does the story take place?
A Fall
B Winter
C Spring
D Summer

2 At what time of day does the story take place?
A Sunrise
B Late at night
C Afternoon
D Sunset

3 What is the weather like in this passage?
A Windy
B Raining
C Snowing
D Cold

4 Which of the following best describes where this story takes place?
A A modern city
B The countryside
C A forest
D A village

Reading Comprehension
Describe Plot, Character, and Setting

Read the passage, and then answer the questions below it. Mark the letter of your answer on a bubble sheet if your teacher provides one; otherwise, circle the letter of the correct answer.

Tom lay thinking. Presently it occurred to him that he wished he was sick; then he could stay home from school. Here was a vague possibility. He canvassed his system. No ailment was found, and he investigated again. This time he thought he could detect colicky symptoms, and he began to encourage them with considerable hope. But they soon grew feeble, and presently died wholly away. He reflected further. Suddenly he discovered something. One of his upper front teeth was loose. This was lucky; he was about to begin to groan, as a "starter," as he called it, when it occurred to him that if he came into court with that argument, his aunt would pull it out, and that would hurt. So he thought he would hold the tooth in reserve for the present, and seek further.

—"Dentistry" by Mark Twain

---

1 What was Tom's motive for faking an illness?
   A He wanted to fool his aunt.
   B He wanted to get his loose tooth pulled.
   C He wanted to stay home from school.
   D He wanted to actually become sick.

2 Which of the following best describes Tom's feelings about school?
   A He is afraid of school.
   B He dislikes school.
   C He enjoys school.
   D He is indifferent toward school.

3 What time of day did this passage take place?
   A Morning
   B Afternoon
   C Evening
   D Late at night

4 What is the central problem for Tom?
   A He has a loose tooth.
   B He does not want to go to school.
   C His aunt wants to pull his tooth.
   D He is actually sick.

5 Tom's main conflict in this passage is with—
   A himself
   B his loose tooth
   C school
   D his aunt

6 What character trait does Tom show in this passage?
   A Honesty
   B Imagination
   C Integrity
   D Respect

Reading Comprehension
Describe Character, Setting, and Mood

Read the passage, and then answer the questions below it. Mark the letter of your answer on a bubble sheet if your teacher provides one; otherwise, circle the letter of the correct answer.

I knew [a] man—let me see—it's forty years ago now—who took an old, damp, rotten set of chambers, in one of the most ancient Inns, that had been shut up and empty for years and years before. There were lots of old women's stories about the place, and it certainly was very far from being a cheerful one; but he was poor, and the rooms were cheap, and that would have been quite a sufficient reason for him, if they had been ten times worse than they really were. He was obliged to take some moldering fixtures that were on the place, and, among the rest, was a great lumbering wooden press for papers, with large glass doors, and a green curtain inside; a pretty useless thing for him, for he had no papers to put in it; and as to his clothes, he carried them about with him, and that wasn't very hard work, either.

— "The Lawyer and the Ghost" by Charles Dickens

1 Which of the following best describes the setting of the story?
   A A new apartment building
   B Old hotel rooms
   C An old woman's place
   D An expensive hotel

2 Which of the following best describes when the story takes place?
   A A week ago
   B A month ago
   C A year ago
   D Many years ago

3 What was the man's motive for staying in this place?
   A He needed a place to store his clothes.
   B The place had a good reputation.
   C The rooms were cheap.
   D He needed a place to set up an office.

4 What character trait does the man show in this passage?
   A Fussy
   B Extravagant
   C Thrifty
   D Cheap

5 What can you infer about the man's wardrobe?
   A He has a worn, but elegant, business suit.
   B He keeps all his clothes packed in several suitcases.
   C He has very expensive clothes.
   D He has the clothes that he is presently wearing.

6 Which best describes the atmosphere in his room?
   A Cheerful
   B Frightening
   C Dreary
   D Cozy

Reading Comprehension

Distinguish Between Fact and Nonfact

Read the passage, and then answer the questions below it. Mark the letter of your answer on a bubble sheet if your teacher provides one; otherwise, circle the letter of the correct answer.

July 21, 1996

What a whirlwind I've been on since the Olympic trials! We arrived in Atlanta at 1:30 P.M. and had processing, which took seven hours. We received lots of great clothes and other goodies. We were also measured for Olympic uniforms, which we will receive later. We finally got to our home at Emory University at 9 P.M. We're staying in a fraternity house until we are competing and then can move into the Olympic Village after that. Jaycie and I are rooming together, sharing a bathroom with Shannon Miller. We decorated our room to make it a little more "homey."

Training is going very well. We train at a private club, except when we have podium training. Tuesday, we had 22,000 cheering fans at our training. I was totally overwhelmed. You just can't imagine the feeling.

—"Olympic Diary" by Amanda Borden

---

1 Which of the following is an OPINION expressed in the diary?
   A Amanda will be given an Olympic uniform.
   B Their first day in Atlanta was very busy.
   C Her room looks very "homey" after she decorated it.
   D Her roommate's name is Jaycie.

2 Which of the following is a FACT expressed in the diary?
   A Her training is going well.
   B The trials were like a whirlwind.
   C The team received great clothes.
   D The team received many gifts when they arrived in Atlanta.

3 Which of the following is an OPINION expressed in the diary?
   A They are staying in a fraternity house at Emory University.
   B It was overwhelming to have 22,000 fans watching training.
   C The fans were cheering.
   D They do not have podium training at the private club.

4 Which of the following is an OPINION expressed in the diary?
   A She has been in a whirlwind since the Olympic trials.
   B They arrived in Atlanta at 1:30 P.M.
   C They were measured for Olympic uniforms.
   D They did not receive their uniforms that day.

Reading Comprehension
Distinguish Between Fact and Nonfact

Read the passage, and then answer the questions below it. Mark the letter of your answer on a bubble sheet if your teacher provides one; otherwise, circle the letter of the correct answer.

We are a very happy family. We consist of Papa, Mamma, Jean, Clara and me. It is papa I am writing about, and I shall have no trouble in not knowing what to say about him, as he is a *very* striking character.

Papa's appearance has been described many times, but very incorrectly. He has beautiful gray hair, not any too thick or any too long, but just right; a Roman nose which greatly improves the beauty of his features; kind blue eyes and a small mustache. He has a wonderfully shaped head and profile. He has a very good figure—in short, he is an extrodinarily fine looking man. All his features are perfect exept that he hasn't extrodinary teeth. His complexion is very fair, and he doesn't ware a beard. He is a very good man and a very funny one. He has got a temper, but we all of us have in this family. He is the loveliest man I ever saw or ever hope to see—and oh, so absentminded.

—"My Papa, Mark Twain" by Susy Clemens

---

1 Which of the following is a FACT from the passage?
 (A) Mark Twain had three daughters.
 B They were a happy family.
 C His wife's name was Susy.
 D He had green eyes.

2 Which of the following is an OPINION from the passage?
 (A) Twain's hair was not too thick or too long.
 B Twain had a Roman nose.
 C Twain had gray hair.
 D Twain had a very fair complexion.

3 Which of the following is a FACT from the passage?
 A Twain was very absent-minded.
 (B) Twain did not wear a beard.
 C Twain's teeth were ugly.
 D Twain was a funny man.

4 Which of the following is an OPINION from the passage?
 A Twain had blue eyes.
 (B) The length of Twain's hair was just right.
 C Twain had gray hair.
 D Twain wore a mustache.

5 Which of the following is a FACT from the passage?
 (A) Twain had blue eyes.
 B Twain had a wonderfully shaped profile.
 C Twain was a fine looking man.
 D All of Twain's features were perfect.

6 Which of the following is an OPINION from the passage?
 A His daughter found it difficult to write about Twain.
 B Twain was very tall.
 (C) Twain had a bad temper.
 D Twain's appearance had been described many times.

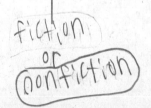

Reading Comprehension
Distinguish Between Fact and Nonfact

Read the passage, and then answer the questions below it. Mark the letter of your answer on a bubble sheet if your teacher provides one; otherwise, circle the letter of the correct answer.

The kids in the spelling bee came from all kinds of backgrounds and from all over the country. That they speak the same language—that a kid from Maine can meet a kid from Oregon and understand him right from the start—that is Noah Webster's gift to us. His little Blue-Backed Speller sold nearly 100 million copies in his lifetime. It wore out printing presses. It was read by nearly every American who could read.

And then, working for twenty-five years, alone and by hand, Noah Webster produced his dictionary—seventy thousand words, including a lot of American words that had never been in a dictionary before: *applesauce, bullfrog, chowder, hickory, skunk.* It was the most valuable piece of scholarship any American ever did.

—"Noah Webster's Dictionary" by Charles Kuralt

---

1 Which of the following is a FACT from the passage?
 A The Blue-Backed Speller sold nearly 25 million copies.
 B Webster wrote the Blue-Backed Speller.
 C The Blue-Backed Speller was written by hand.
 D Only kids from the same background could participate in the spelling bees.

2 Which of the following is a FACT from the passage?
 A Webster worked with a staff to create his dictionary.
 B It took Webster less than 25 years to write his dictionary.
 C The Blue-Backed Speller sold nearly 100 million copies.
 D The word "skunk" had been in a dictionary before Webster's.

3 Which of the following is a FACT from the passage?
 A Webster's dictionary had 70,000 words in it.
 B Webster worked with machines to produce his dictionary.
 C Webster's dictionary only included words that had been in a dictionary before.
 D Webster's dictionary was the most valuable piece an American ever wrote.

4 Which of the following is an OPINION from the passage?
 A Webster's dictionary contained 70,000 words.
 B Webster was responsible for all people speaking the same language.
 C Webster worked alone on the Blue-Backed Speller.
 D It took Webster 25 years to produce his dictionary.

Reading Comprehension

Distinguish Between Fact and Nonfact

Read the passage, and then answer the questions below it. Mark the letter of your answer on a bubble sheet if your teacher provides one; otherwise, circle the letter of the correct answer.

The central problem in designing the Internet was finding a way for different kinds of computers all over the country to talk to one another. ARPA solved this problem with Internet protocols. Protocols are sets of rules that standardize how something is done, so that everyone knows what to expect. For example, think of any game you've played and the rules that went with that game. The rules of the game tell you how many players you can have, what order you play in, what's allowed and what's not allowed, and how to keep score. Once you know the rules, you can play with people very different from you. Internet protocols are like game rules: they set up standard procedures for computers to follow so that they can communicate with each other.

—"How the Internet Works" by Kerry Cochrane

---

1 Which of the following is a FACT from the essay?
   A Protocols were unable to solve the Internet's problems.
   B Protocols are a set of rules that describe manners for programmers to use.
   C ARPA was unable to solve the problem with the Internet.
   D The central problem with the Internet was that different kinds of computers could not communicate with each other.

2 Which of the following is a FACT from the essay?
   A The ARPA is an organization of computer programmers.
   B The ARPA established protocols to solve the Internet's problem.
   C Protocols are the most important contribution made to computers.
   D The ARPA is a prestigious organization to belong to.

3 Which of the following is NOT a FACT from the essay?
   A ARPA set up standard procedures for the Internet.
   B Protocols solved the Internet's problems.
   C ARPA created the Internet.
   D Protocols allowed computers to communicate on the Internet.

4 Which of the following is NOT a FACT from the essay?
   A There are no standardized rules for the Internet.
   B Protocols standardize how things are done on the Internet.
   C Internet protocols are like game rules.
   D Computers are able to communicate with each other.

Writing Skills
Recognize Appropriate Sentence Construction

Read the passage, and then answer the questions below it. Mark the letter of your answer on a bubble sheet if your teacher provides one; otherwise, circle the letter of the correct answer.

In the drama. _The Phantom Tollbooth._ Milo is bored. He is a restless boy who is
1
never satisfied with what he has. Milo never knows what to do with himself.

Nothing interests Milo until he enters the Lands Beyond through a secret tollbooth.
2
In this fantasy world, Milo meets many fantastical, humorous characters. These
3
characters show him how to enjoy and value even the smallest things. Such as
words and numbers. This lesson changes Milo's whole, outlook on life.
4

1 What is the BEST way to write underlined section (1)?
  A In the drama, _The Phantom Tollbooth;_ Milo is bored.
  B In the drama _The Phantom Tollbooth._ Milo is bored.
  C In the drama _The Phantom Tollbooth,_ Milo is bored.
  D Correct as is

2 What is the BEST way to write underlined section (2)?
  A Nothing interests Milo until; he enters the Lands Beyond through a secret tollbooth.
  B Nothing interests Milo. Until he enters the Lands Beyond through a secret tollbooth.
  C Nothing interests Milo until. He enters the Lands Beyond— through a secret tollbooth.
  D Correct as is

3 What is the BEST way to write underlined section (3)?
  A These characters show him how to enjoy and value even the smallest. Things such as words and numbers.
  B These characters show him how to enjoy, and value, even the smallest things such as words, and numbers.
  C These characters show him how to enjoy and value even the smallest things, such as words and numbers.
  D Correct as is

4 What is the BEST way to write underlined section (4)?
  A This lesson changes Milo's whole outlook on life.
  B This lesson, changes Milo's whole outlook on life.
  C This lesson changes Milo's whole outlook, on life.
  D Correct as is

Writing Skills

Recognize Appropriate Sentence Construction

Read the passage, and then answer the questions below it. Mark the letter of your answer on a bubble sheet if your teacher provides one; otherwise, circle the letter of the correct answer.

Staging, the art of putting a play on the stage and making it come to life for
1
the audience. It includes the use of sets, costumes, lighting, sound effects,
2
special effects, and props.

The dialogue, and stage directions, provide information, about the staging.
3
These elements are usually extremely important to the action of the play. Cannot
4
be left out or changed.

---

1 What is the BEST way to write underlined section (1)?

  A Staging is the art of putting a play on the stage. And making it come to life for the audience.

  B Staging is the art of putting a play on the stage and making it come to life for the audience.

  C Making it come to life for the audience, staging, the art of putting a play on the stage.

  D Correct as is

2 What is the BEST way to write underlined section (2)?

  A It includes the use of sets costumes lighting sound effects special effects, and props.

  B It includes the use of sets and costumes and lighting and sound effects and special effects and props.

  C It includes the use of sets. Costumes, lighting, sound effects, special effects, and props.

  D Correct as is

3 What is the BEST way to write underlined section (3)?

  A The dialogue and stage directions. Provide information about the staging.

  B The dialogue and stage directions provide information. About the staging.

  C The dialogue and stage directions provide information about the staging.

  D Correct as is

4 What is the BEST way to write underlined section (4)?

  A These elements are usually extremely important to the action of the play, and, cannot be left out or changed.

  B These elements are usually extremely important to the action of the play and cannot be left out or changed.

  C These elements are usually extremely important to the action. The play cannot be left out or changed.

  D Correct as is

Writing Skills
Recognize Appropriate Sentence Construction

Read the passage, and then answer the questions below it. Mark the letter of your answer on a bubble sheet if your teacher provides one; otherwise, circle the letter of the correct answer.

. . . Ancient forests mighty rivers and icy plains stretched for miles without a
         1
road in sight. Like the orphan Anne of Green Gables from Lucy M. Montgomery's
                  2
novels. Canada's early settlers faced life on their own.

  In the 1600s, adventurers arrived from France to trap beavers for their valuable
         3
fur. . . . In 1763, after the Seven Years War with France. Britain gained control of
              4
Canada.

---

1 What is the BEST way to write underlined section (1)?
  A Ancient forests, mighty rivers, and icy plains. Stretched for miles without a road in sight.
  B Ancient forests, mighty rivers, and icy plains stretched for miles without a road in sight.
  C Ancient forests, mighty rivers, and icy plains stretched. For miles, without a road in sight.
  D Correct as is

2 What is the BEST way to write underlined section (2)?
  A Canada's early settlers facing life on their own like the orphan Anne of Green Gables from Lucy M. Montgomery's novels.
  B Like the orphan Anne of Green Gables, from Lucy M. Montgomery's novels. Canada's early settlers faced life on their own.
  C Like the orphan Anne of Green Gables from Lucy M. Montgomery's novels,

Canada's early settlers faced life on their own.
  D Correct as is

3 What is the BEST way to write underlined section (3)?
  A In the 1600s adventurers, arrived from France to trap beavers for their valuable fur.
  B In the 1600s, adventurers arrived from France to trap beavers. For their valuable fur.
  C In the 1600s, adventurers arrived from France. To trap beavers for their valuable fur.
  D Correct as is

4 What is the BEST way to write underlined section (4)?
  A In 1763, after the Seven Years War with France, Britain gained control of Canada.
  B In 1763 after the Seven Years War with France. Britain gained control of Canada.
  C In 1763, after the Seven Years War, with France, Britain gained control of Canada.
  D Correct as is

Writing Skills

Recognize Appropriate Sentence Construction

Read the passage, and then answer the questions below it. Mark the letter of your answer on a bubble sheet if your teacher provides one; otherwise, circle the letter of the correct answer.

. . . Since a radio play is meant to be listened to but not watched. The play's
    1

action is revealed through its dialogue. . . . All drama uses dialogue to describe
                       2

"off stage" or "off screen" action.

. . . The character of Grandpa is revealed. Through the memories of his
    3

grandson, Monaghan. . . .

---

1 What is the BEST way to write underlined section (1)?

  A Since a radio play is meant to be listened to, but not watched. The play's action is revealed through its dialogue.

  B Since a radio play is meant to be listened to but not watched, the play's action is revealed through its dialogue.

  C Since, a radio play is meant to be listened to, but not watched the play's action is revealed through its dialogue.

  D Correct as is

2 What is the BEST way to write underlined section (2)?

  A All drama uses dialogue. To describe "off stage" or "off screen" action.

  B All drama uses dialogue, to describe "off stage" or "off screen" action.

  C All drama uses dialogue to describe "off stage," or, "off screen," action.

  D Correct as is

3 What is the BEST way to write underlined section (3)?

  A The character of Grandpa is revealed. Through the memories of his grandson. Monaghan.

  B The character of Grandpa is revealed through the memories of his grandson. Monaghan is the name of the grandson.

  C The character of Grandpa is revealed through the memories of his grandson, Monaghan.

  D Correct as is

Writing Skills
Recognize Appropriate Usage

Read the passage, and then answer the questions below it. Mark the letter of your answer on a bubble sheet if your teacher provides one; otherwise, circle the letter of the correct answer.

T.S. Eliot ____(1)____ a poet who made poetry sound more like ____(2)____ spoken

language. He also gave poetry the nervous rhythms of the early twentieth

century, a time of rapid change. Eliot's poetry is often very ____(3)____. However, he

also wrote the humorous poems that appear in *Old Possum's Book of Practical*

Cats. This book, which includes "The Naming of Cats," inspired the Broadway

musical *Cats.*

Over a period of many generations, Eliot's family moved from England to New

England and then to St. Louis, Missouri. In his own life, Eliot reversed this

pattern. He was born in St. Louis and went to college in New England. Then

____(4)____ traveled to England, settling there and ____(5)____ a citizen of that country.

---

1 Choose the word or group of
words that belongs in space (1).
A has been
B is
C was
D will be

2 Choose the word or group of
words that belongs in space (2).
A ordinary
B ordinarily
C more ordinary
D ordinariest

3 Choose the word or group of
words that belongs in space (3).
A seriously
B seriousness
C serious
D more serious

4 Choose the word that belongs in
space (4).
A they
B them
C it
D he

5 Choose the word or group of
words that belongs in space (5).
A becomes
B becoming
C will become
D became

Writing Skills
Recognize Appropriate Usage

Read the passage, and then answer the questions below it. Mark the letter of your answer on a bubble sheet if your teacher provides one; otherwise, circle the letter of the correct answer.

In "The Walrus and the Carpenter," Lewis Carroll combines nonsense and narrative. Carroll tells how a Walrus __(1)__ some young oysters into trusting him. __(2)__ convinces them to leave the ocean and __(3)__ him and his __(4)__ companion, the Carpenter, on a walk. After __(5)__ the oysters far from home, the Walrus and the Carpenter eat all the foolish oysters. Most of the stanzas are full of playful nonsense and help __(6)__ humor to the poem. However, the betrayal described in the last part of the poem adds an element of sadness as well. In this poem, Carroll brings us into a world very different from the everyday.

---

1 Choose the word or group of words that belongs in space (1).
  A trick
  B tricked
  C will trick
  D tricks

2 Choose the word that belongs in space (2).
  A He
  B She
  C They
  D It

3 Choose the word or group of words that belongs in space (3).
  A joins
  B to join
  C joined
  D is joining

4 Choose the word that belongs in space (4).
  A grumpily
  B grumpy
  C grump
  D grumpiness

5 Choose the word or group of words that belongs in space (5).
  A lures
  B lured
  C luring
  D had lured

6 Choose the word or group of words that belongs in space (6).
  A adding
  B adds
  C to add
  D added

Writing Skills
Recognize Appropriate Usage

Read the passage, and then answer the questions below it. Mark the letter of your answer on a bubble sheet if your teacher provides one; otherwise, circle the letter of the correct answer.

In "The Concrete Cat," Dorthi Charles draws an __(1)__ picture of a cat using

words. Each word is not just a word; it also takes on the shape of the feature it

__(2)__. The ending of this __(3)__ poem surprises the reader with the

realization that the cat __(4)__ a mouse. "The Concrete Cat" is very __(5)__ in

that it contains only nouns; and it has no rhyme or punctuation. It does have an

irregular kind of rhythm, but it is the placement of the words that __(6)__ most

of the poem's meaning.

---

1 Choose the word that belongs in space (1).
A actuality
B actual
C actually
D actualize

2 Choose the word or group of words that belongs in space (2).
A represents
B represented
C is representing
D represent

3 Choose the word that belongs in space (3).
A lightheartedly
B lightheartedness
C lightheart
D lighthearted

4 Choose the word or group of words that belongs in space (4).
A has eaten
B eaten
C will eat
D had ate

5 Choose the word or group of words that belongs in space (5).
A unusually
B unusual
C unused
D unused to

6 Choose the word or group of words that belongs in space (6).
A was communicating
B communicated
C communicates
D to communicate

Writing Skills

Recognize Appropriate Usage

Read the passage, and then answer the questions below it. Mark the letter
of your answer on a bubble sheet if your teacher provides one; otherwise,
circle the letter of the correct answer.

Brooks has written many poems about her neighbors and neighborhood in

Chicago. She ____(1)____ lived most of her life in that large midwestern city. When

____(2)____ was only seventeen, Brooks ____(3)____ writing poetry. As a teenager, she

had her poetry published in a well-known magazine. Her poems were also

____(4)____ in a local newspaper, the *Chicago Defender*.

Eventually, she ____(5)____ a well-respected poet. She ____(6)____ the Pulitzer Prize

for her second book, *Annie Allen* (1949).

1 Choose the word that belongs in
space (1).
 A had
 B have
 C has
 D having

2 Choose the word that belongs in
space (2).
 A she
 B he
 C it
 D they

3 Choose the word or group of
words that belongs in space (3).
 A starts
 B will start
 C has started
 D started

4 Choose the word or group of
words that belongs in space (4).
 A are published
 B were published
 C published
 D will be published

5 Choose the word or group of
words that belongs in space (5).
 A will become
 B has become
 C have become
 D became

6 Choose the word or group of
words that belongs in space (6).
 A will receive
 B receives
 C had received
 D received

Writing Skills

Recognize Appropriate Usage

Read the passage, and then answer the questions below it. Mark the letter of your answer on a bubble sheet if your teacher provides one; otherwise, circle the letter of the correct answer.

Langston Hughes brought the rhythms of African American music and speech to American poetry. Raised in the Midwest, he ___(1)___ the world on merchant ships as a ___(2)___ man. Then, he settled in New York City's African American community of Harlem. There, ___(3)___ felt the influence of musical styles like jazz and the blues. ___(4)___ his best-known collections of poetry are *The Weary Blues* (1926) and *The Dream Keeper* (1932).

Hughes kept a childlike sense of wonder throughout his life. It's not surprising that he ___(5)___ his first poems in a magazine for African American children. "April Rain Song," with its ___(6)___ wonder at the rain, appeared in the 1921 issue.

---

1 Choose the word or group of words that belongs in space (1).
A travels
B traveled
C traveler
D will travel

2 Choose the word that belongs in space (2).
A young
B youth
C youngster
D youthfully

3 Choose the word that belongs in space (3).
A he
B she
C it
D they

4 Choose the word that belongs in space (4).
A Beside
B On
C Among
D Upon

5 Choose the word or group of words that belongs in space (5).
A publishes
B publisher
C is publishing
D published

6 Choose the word that belongs in space (6).
A youth
B youthfully
C youthfulness
D youthful

Writing Skills

Recognize Appropriate Usage

Read the passage, and then answer the questions below it. Mark the letter of your answer on a bubble sheet if your teacher provides one; otherwise, circle the letter of the correct answer.

In his poem "Wind and water and stone," Octavio Paz tells how these three

elements ___(1)___ a game with one another. This game is more than a poetic

idea. The imaginary hands of these elements have shaped the land of Mexico.

Wind's ___(2)___ hands block or bring the rain. Counterclockwise winds create

a dry climate in the north of Mexico. Yet hurricanes drench the eastern and

western coasts from August through October. In the south, air masses ___(3)___

heavy rains in late spring and summer.

Mexico has a few large rivers that reach through the land ___(4)___ fingers. The

largest in the dry north is the Rio Bravo del Norte, ___(5)___ in the United States

as the Rio Grande.

---

1 Choose the word that belongs in space (1).
A plays
B were playing
C play
D player

2 Choose the word or group of words that belongs in space (2).
A invisible
B invisibility
C invisibly
D most invisible

3 Choose the word or group of words that belongs in space (3).
A brought
B bring
C had brought
D brings

4 Choose the word that belongs in space (4).
A likes
B likely
C likeness
D like

5 Choose the word that belongs in space (5).
A knowable
B known
C knowingly
D know

Writing Skills

Recognize Appropriate Usage

Read the passage, and then answer the questions below it. Mark the letter of your answer on a bubble sheet if your teacher provides one; otherwise, circle the letter of the correct answer.

Instead of ____(1)____ poetic words, the Englishman William Wordsworth used everyday language ____(2)____ about everyday things. He showed that what is ____(3)____ is really extraordinary. His ideas about poetry ____(4)____ by his experiences in the ____(5)____ Lake District in northwestern England, where he grew up and lived much of his life.

Wordsworth ____(6)____ that poets are just like everyone else, only they are a little more sensitive to their surroundings.

1 Choose the word or group of words that belongs in space (1).
   A fancier
   B fancy
   C most fancy
   D fancifully

2 Choose the word or group of words that belongs in space (2).
   A to write
   B is writing
   C will write
   D wrote

3 Choose the word that belongs in space (3).
   A ordinarily
   B ordinariness
   C ordinary
   D ordinance

4 Choose the word or group of words that belongs in space (4).
   A were inspiring
   B were inspired
   C inspirational
   D inspiration

5 Choose the word that belongs in space (5).
   A beautifully
   B beautify
   C beautification
   D beautiful

6 Choose the word or group of words that belongs in space (6).
   A believes
   B believer
   C believed
   D will believe

Writing Skills

Recognize Appropriate Spelling, Capitalization, and Punctuation

Read the passage, and then answer the questions below it. Mark the letter of your answer on a bubble sheet if your teacher provides one; otherwise, circle the letter of the correct answer.

Long ago, an emperor who cared more about clothes than anything else was fooled by two rascals pretending to be weavers they claimed they could weave

1

exquisite clothes that became invisible to anyone stupid . . . thinking such

2

clothes could help him identify incompetent or foolish Underlings, the emperor

3

paid the rascals, who pretended to weave the clothes. His ministers monitered

4

the progress, and each saw nothing on the looms, but fear of being branded stupid or unfit prompted each to come back with a glowing report. When the clothes were presented, the emperor too saw nothing, but he too pretended he could. As he moved in a grand prosession, everyone praised his clothes . . .

5

1 Which type of error, if any, appears in underlined section 1?
   A Spelling
   B Capitalization
   C Punctuation
   D No error

2 Which type of error, if any, appears in underlined section 2?
   A Spelling
   B Capitalization
   C Punctuation
   D No error

3 Which type of error, if any, appears in underlined section 3?
   A Spelling
   B Capitalization
   C Punctuation
   D No error

4 Which type of error, if any, appears in underlined section 4?
   A Spelling
   B Capitalization
   C Punctuation
   D No error

5 Which type of error, if any, appears in underlined section 5?
   A Spelling
   B Capitalization
   C Punctuation
   D No error

Writing Skills

Recognize Appropriate Spelling, Capitalization, and Punctuation

Read the passage, and then answer the questions below it. Mark the letter of your answer on a bubble sheet if your teacher provides one; otherwise, circle the letter of the correct answer.

In the forest, he Lion was scaring all the small animals with his great roar, ME

AND MYSELF, ME AND MYSELF. the small animals took the problem to Bruh
                          1

Bear and Bruh Rabbit, who went to talk with the lion. He Lion ensisted that he
                                                             2

was King of the forest and could roar when he pleased. Bruh Rabbit told him that
    3

the real king of the forest was Man, . . . When he Lion wanted to see man, Bruh

Rabbit took him all over. . . . Finnaly they came upon a man, who was about
                                 4

twenty-one years old. When he Lion roared at him Man raised his big gun and
                          5

shot at he Lion, who flew off.

---

1 Which type of error, if any, appears in underlined section 1?
A Spelling
B Capitalization
C Punctuation
D No error

2 Which type of error, if any, appears in underlined section 2?
A Spelling
B Capitalization
C Punctuation
D No error

3 Which type of error, if any, appears in underlined section 3?
A Spelling
B Capitalization
C Punctuation
D No error

4 Which type of error, if any, appears in underlined section 4?
A Spelling
B Capitalization
C Punctuation
D No error

5 Which type of error, if any, appears in underlined section 5?
A Spelling
B Capitalization
C Punctuation
D No error

Writing Skills

Recognize Appropriate Spelling, Capitalization, and Punctuation

Read the passage, and then answer the questions below it. Mark the letter of your answer on a bubble sheet if your teacher provides one; otherwise, circle the letter of the correct answer.

One of the most popular <u>greek myths tells the</u> adventures of the hero Perseus.
                                            1
His brave deeds are the subject of <u>the story, The Gorgon's Head.</u> <u>To appreciate a</u>
                                                          2   3
<u>myth, you must understand the culture from which it comes.</u> In ancient Greece,

strength and bravery in battle were the most valued qualities. You will see these

qualities in Perseus, the hero of <u>*The gorgon's head.*</u> To some extent, Perseus's
                                                        4
struggle <u>explanes how ancient</u> peoples came to hold his traits in such high
                        5
esteem.

---

1 Which type of error, if any, appears in underlined section 1?
  A Spelling
  B Capitalization
  C Punctuation
  D No error

2 Which type of error, if any, appears in underlined section 2?
  A Spelling
  B Capitalization
  C Punctuation
  D No error

3 Which type of error, if any, appears in underlined section 3?
  A Spelling
  B Capitalization
  C Punctuation
  D No error

4 Which type of error, if any, appears in underlined section 4?
  A Spelling
  B Capitalization
  C Punctuation
  D No error

5 Which type of error, if any, appears in underlined section 5?
  A Spelling
  B Capitalization
  C Punctuation
  D No error

Writing Skills

Recognize Appropriate Spelling, Capitalization, and Punctuation

Read the passage, and then answer the questions below it. Mark the letter of your answer on a bubble sheet if your teacher provides one; otherwise, circle the letter of the correct answer.

One day <u>king Gorilla</u> offers a pot of gold to anyone who can eat what looks
1
like a mound of black dust in one day. <u>Lion claims he can eat it in an hour</u>
2
<u>Leopard in half an hour and Hippopotamus, in one gulp.</u> When they try, however,

they cannot do it, for it turns out the mound is black <u>peper. Then</u> Monkey says
3
he can do it if he can lie down and rest in the tall grass between mouthfuls. He

seemingly follows this procedure until the mound of pepper is gone, and King

Gorilla announces him the winner. <u>Leopard however spies hundreds of lookalike</u>
4
monkeys hiding in the tall grass and realizes that each has come forward and

taken one mouthful. <u>Furius, he chases the monkeys</u>, and the others join in.
5

1 Which type of error, if any, appears in underlined section 1?
A Spelling
B Capitalization
C Punctuation
D No error

2 Which type of error, if any, appears in underlined section 2?
A Spelling
B Capitalization
C Punctuation
D No error

3 Which type of error, if any, appears in underlined section 3?
A Spelling
B Capitalization
C Punctuation
D No error

4 Which type of error, if any, appears in underlined section 4?
A Spelling
B Capitalization
C Punctuation
D No error

5 Which type of error, if any, appears in underlined section 5?
A Spelling
B Capitalization
C Punctuation
D No error

Writing Skills

Recognize Appropriate Spelling, Capitalization, and Punctuation

Read the passage, and then answer the questions below it. Mark the letter of your answer on a bubble sheet if your teacher provides one; otherwise, circle the letter of the correct answer.

"Loo-Wit, The Fire-Keeper" is a <u>Native american myth</u> from the <u>Nisqually</u>
                         1   2

<u>indians.</u> The myth reveals how the Nisqually explained the earth's formations,

characteristics, and <u>whether when</u> scientific knowledge was unknown. The myth
                        3

also reveals the Nisqually belief that greed and disrespect for the earth lead to

misfortune. <u>Loo-Wit the only member of the tribe who is not greedy is rewarded</u>
               4

by the Creator and turned <u>into a peece-keeping</u> volcano—<u>sure to erupt only</u>
                           5   6

<u>when the Earth is not treated with respect and the people do not "keep their</u>

<u>hearts good."</u>

---

1 Which type of error, if any, appears in underlined section 1?
A Spelling
B Capitalization
C Punctuation
D No error

2 Which type of error, if any, appears in underlined section 2?
A Spelling
B Capitalization
C Punctuation
D No error

3 Which type of error, if any, appears in underlined section 3?
A Spelling
B Capitalization
C Punctuation
D No error

4 Which type of error, if any, appears in underlined section 4?
A Spelling
B Capitalization
C Punctuation
D No error

5 Which type of error, if any, appears in underlined section 5?
A Spelling
B Capitalization
C Punctuation
D No error

6 Which type of error, if any, appears in underlined section 6?
A Spelling
B Capitalization
C Punctuation
D No error

English: Reading/Literature and Research

•••

Directions: Read each passage. Then read each question about the passage. Decide which is the best answer to each question. Mark the space on your answer sheet for the answer you have chosen.

SAMPLE

Field Trip

Our teacher, Mrs. Yost, said we could go on a field trip if we found affordable transportation. I asked my mother to call bus companies to find the best price. Then I organized a bake sale to raise money. We will hold the bake sale on Saturday, but if it rains, we will hold it on Sunday.

"But what if it rains cats and dogs on Saturday *and* Sunday?" Ellen asked.

"We'll have to worry about that on Sunday, won't we?" I said.

A From the way the word <u>transportation</u> is used, what do you think the word <u>transport</u> means?
A get permission
B travel from one place to another
C visit a park or museum
D raise money by selling candy bars

B The phrase "rains cats and dogs" means that it would rain—
F money
G household pets
H hard
J frequently

Directions: Read the passage, and answer the questions that follow.

from **The Lawyer and the Ghost**
Charles Dickens

1 I knew [a] man—let me see—it's forty years ago now—who took an old, damp, rotten set of chambers, in one of the most ancient Inns, that had been shut up and empty for years and years before. There were lots of old women's stories about the place, and it certainly was very far from being a cheerful one; but he was poor, and the rooms were cheap, and that would have been quite a <u>sufficient</u> reason for him, if they had been ten times worse than they really were. He was obliged to take some moldering fixtures that were on the place, and, among the rest, was a great lumbering wooden press for papers, with large glass doors, and a green curtain inside; a pretty useless thing for him, for he had no papers to put in it; and as to his clothes, he carried them about with him, and that wasn't very hard work, either.

2 Well, he had moved in all his furniture—it wasn't quite a truckfull—and sprinkled it about the room, so as to make the four chairs look as much like a dozen as possible, and was sitting down before the fire at night, . . . when his eyes encountered the glass doors of the wooded press. "Ah!" says he—"If I hadn't been obliged to take that ugly article at the old broker's valuation, I might have got something comfortable for the money. I'll tell you what it is, old fellow," he said, speaking aloud to the press, just because he had got nothing else to speak to—"If it wouldn't cost more to break up your old carcass, than it would ever be worth afterwards, I'd have a fire out of you, in less than no time."

3 He had hardly spoken the words, when a sound resembling a faint groan, appeared to issue from the interior of the case. It startled him at first, but thinking, on a moment's reflection, that it must be some young fellow in the next chambers, who had been dining out, he put his feet on the fender, and raised the poker to stir the fire. At that moment, the sound was repeated: and one of the glass doors slowly opening, disclosed a pale and emaciated figure in soiled and worn apparel, standing erect in the press. The figure was tall and thin, and the countenance expressive of care and anxiety; but there was something in the hue of the skin, and gaunt and unearthly appearance of the whole form, which no being of this world was ever seen to wear.

4 "Who are you?" said the new tenant, turning very pale, poising the poker in his hand, however, and taking a very decent aim at the countenance of the figure—"Who are you?"

5 "Don't throw that poker at me," replied the form—"If you hurled it with ever so sure an aim, it would pass through me, without resistance, and <u>expend</u> its force on the wood behind. I am a spirit."

1 **Expend** is to *consume* as *distribute*
is to
- **A** give up
- **B** give out
- **C** get back
- **D** get away

2 **The main idea of the first paragraph of
the passage is that—**
- **F** The man who moved to the Inn did
not know many women so he didn't
know their stories.
- **G** Forty years ago, the man lived in a
place that was not nearly as nice as
where he lives now.
- **H** The poor man moved to an unpleasant
place that no one had lived in for a
long time.
- **J** The man brought furniture to his new
home that was of little use to him.

3 **What is the man's original purpose for
moving to the chambers at the Inn?**
- **A** He was a writer of ghost stories and
was looking for inspiration.
- **B** He wanted to impress the women who
knew stories about the place.
- **C** He loved old buildings and wanted to
restore his chambers' former beauty.
- **D** He needed a place to live and was
unable to afford better chambers.

4 **The root of the word *reflection* is
-flect-, which means "to think or
ponder something." With the prefix
re- and the suffix *-ion*, the whole word
can be defined as—**
- **F** thinking about something
- **G** thinking about something again
- **H** thinking about something for the
first time
- **J** not thinking about something

5 **When the man calls the wooden press
"old carcass," he is using—**
- **A** simile
- **B** personification
- **C** metaphor
- **D** alliteration

6 **The author *probably* wrote this
passage to—**
- **F** inform the reader about life in
the 1800s
- **G** describe a wooden press
- **H** entertain the reader with a fictional
tale
- **J** show how some poor people used
to live

7 **You can tell from the passage that the
word sufficient means—**
- **A** suffering
- **B** old-fashioned
- **C** not worth a cent
- **D** enough

| The man moves into a new place. |
| ↓ |
| He thinks about his wooden press and talks to it. |
| ↓ |
| |
| The figure reveals that he is a spirit. |

8 **The statement that *best* completes
the blank box is—**
- **F** He feels that he was pressured to
buy the wooden press.
- **G** He learns how to use the wooden
press.
- **H** A figure appears in the wooden press.
- **J** He throws a poker at the wooden
press.

Directions: Read the passages, and answer the questions that follow.

Promoting Fitness in Schools

In the two articles below, students from the Brentwood School District express their opinions about a recent change in school policy.

Article 1

1 At its meeting last week, the Brentwood School Board decided to require student athletes to attend Physical Education (P.E.) classes. As an athlete, I feel this requirement is unfair.

2 Playing a team sport at school requires the same type of activity (physical exercise) as a P.E. course. Athletes may exhaust or injure themselves if they take part in both activities. In addition, the time spent in P.E. courses can be put to use by coaches as training time. That way, athletes would not have to spend so much time training after school and would have more time to study. Finally, as I understand it, P.E. courses are supposed to develop an interest in athletics. Students who take part in team sports already have this interest. For athletes, P.E. is unnecessary, and it might even be harmful—both physically and academically.

3 I hope the Brentwood School District will consider the time and effort student athletes put into their teams and reconsider its decision.

—Sandra Alvarado

Article 2

1 I would like to applaud the Brentwood School District for its decision to require student athletes to take part in Physical Education (P.E.) courses.

2 For too long, athletes have had a special, separate status among students. Taking part in P.E. classes will help bring athletes and other students closer together. Our star players will have the opportunity to share their knowledge about sports and other students will benefit. P.E. courses will also be good places for athletes to learn. Instead of playing only one or two sports, athletes will have the opportunity to try out a variety of activities. They may even find a new team to join!

3 I am very pleased with the results of the school board's vote and hope they will <u>uphold</u> their decision.

—Andrew Chang

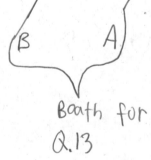

Booth for
Q.13

9 Which of these is the *best* question to ask about the reasons Sandra and Andrew wrote their articles?

  A What sport does Sandra play?

  B What sports does Andrew want athletes to learn more about?

  C What do both writers want students to have the opportunity to do?

  D What is the "special, separate status" that athletes had enjoyed?

10 What do you think Andrew's response to Sandra's article would be?

  F He would agree with her because he always worries that athletes don't have enough time to study.

  G He would agree with her because he also plays on sports teams.

  H He would disagree with her because he thinks P.E. classes give all students opportunities to learn.

  J He would disagree with her because he is a member of the school board.

11 If Sandra wanted to add information from other sources to her argument, she should look for articles that—

  A explain which sports most schools offer

  B give the schedules for athletic events

  C describe an average P.E. class

  D list statistics about athletes who are injured in P.E. classes

12 What does Sandra mean when she says P.E. classes could be academically harmful for athletes?

  F P.E. classes would be difficult for athletes and they might fail.

  G P.E. classes take up time athletes could use to study for their other classes.

  H Athletes who take P.E. classes would have to drop out of one of their other courses.

  J P.E. classes would create too much homework for athletes.

13 According to Article 2, athletes need to—

  A spend more time with other students

  B join more teams

  C use the time spent in gym classes for training or doing their homework

  D spend more time reading

14 The word <u>uphold</u> in Article 2 means—

  F reverse

  G support

  H lift

  J drive

15 From his article you can tell that Andrew Chang—

  A wants the best situation for nonathletes only

  B does not like athletes

  C hopes the school board will change its decision

  D wants to bring students closer together

16 Both articles were written in order to—

  F complain about athletic teams

  G explain why the school board should change its decision

  H explain why the school board should not change its decision

  J express the writers' opinions about a school board decision

from "The Spider Woman"
A Navajo Folk Tale

1 "What is this that you do, Grandmother?" the Kisani girl asked.

2 "It is a blanket I weave," the old woman replied.

3 "Does it have a name, Grandmother?"

4 "I will name it Black Design Blanket." And this became the . . . first blanket of the Navajo. . . .

5 "It is late and I must be leaving," the girl said.

6 "Please. Spend the night with me, my grandchild." This the Kisani girl agreed to and began to settle for the night. . . .

7 Spider Woman made some dumplings out of grass seeds and fed the girl and the next morning started weaving another blanket. She worked so fast that she finished it that day. It was square and as long as her arm and she named this new blanket Pretty Design Blanket. The girl watched her all day and stayed there a second night, and the following morning the Spider Woman started still another blanket. She finished this blanket, which she called White Striped Blanket, that day, and on the fourth morning she began another. This was a "Beautiful Design Skirt" such as Yeibichai dancers and Snake dancers wear, and was white with figures in black.

8 The next morning the Kisani girl went back to the hogan where she had been staying and asked the Navajos for some cotton in three colors—yellow, black, and white. After cotton had been given to her, she put up a loom . . . the way Navajo women do now and began a blanket. Her blanket was about half done when another Kisani woman came in and looked at the loom and the design. . . .

9 "Where did you learn to do that?" the Kisani woman asked. "I did this on my own thought," answered the girl. "It is called a Black Design Blanket."

10 . . . [T]he next morning she put up her loom again and asked for more cotton to weave. She made a Beautiful Design Skirt the same day. It was finished when two Kisani men came in and asked to see the blankets she had made. One examined the Beautiful Design Blanket very carefully. The second man observed the Black Design weaving. They then returned to their homes and made looms, copying the designs they had learned.

11 The girl only made two blankets and then went back to the Spider Woman's house. Spider Woman was now weaving a wicker water jar and . . . a big carrying basket such as Navajo women used to carry on their backs. The Kisani girl learned to make the basket and then the water jar. "When I went back," she told the Spider Woman, "I showed the people how to make blankets like yours. Now I will go back and make carrying baskets and water jars."

12 "That is good," said Spider Woman. "I am glad you have taught them. But whenever you make a blanket, you must leave a hole in the middle the way I do. For if you do not, your weaving thoughts will be trapped within the cotton and not only will it bring you bad luck, but it will drive you mad."

13 The girl went back to her hogan and made a carrying basket and a water jar. . . .

14 The Navajo women watched her, and soon they were all making carrying baskets and they learned to make water jars and blankets too. . . . [T]he Navajo women . . . kept on with their blanket weaving. And they always left the spider-hole in the center of the weaving pattern . . . And that's true, even today.

17 You can tell from the passage that—
A the Kisani girl was afraid of Spider Woman
B Navajos did not make designs in their blankets before the Kisani girl showed them how
C other Navajo women were jealous of the Kisani girl
D men did most of the weaving of blankets before the Kisani girl returned from visiting Spider Woman

18 Which of the following is the *best* summary of the passage?
F The Kisani girl decides to pay a visit to Spider Woman, who is busy weaving blankets.
G The Navajo men and women copy the looms made by the Kisani girl and begin to weave.
H The Kisani girl learns to weave blankets and baskets from Spider Woman and teaches the other Navajos.
J The Kisani girl learns from Spider Woman that a hole should always be left in the center of Najavo blankets.

19 Based on information from this passage, the reader can predict that the Navajos in this village probably—
A grew to dislike the Kisani girl
B abandoned their traditions eventually
C started to put spider holes in their blankets as well
D went to visit Spider Woman themselves

20 Which of these happened after the girl went to Spider Woman a second time?
F The girl learned to make a Beautiful Design Skirt.
G The girl made a carrying basket.
H The other Navajos made looms for weaving.
J Spider Woman made her some dumplings.

21 Which of the following is a *fact* in this passage?
A Spider Woman was frightening.
B Navajo blankets are among the most beautiful in the world.
C The Kisani girl was too tired to learn to make blankets properly.
D Navajo women used to carry water on their backs.

22 The Navajo weavers leave a hole in the middle of their blankets to—
F protect them from bad luck and madness
G let smoke through
H make sure their blankets are not better than Spider Woman's
J keep the blankets from unraveling

23 From this story, you can conclude that people learned to weave by—
A reading books
B attending weaving classes
C studying blankets in museums
D watching others

24 The information contained in this passage could help you write a report about—
F spiders
G blankets
H Navajo traditions
J grandmothers

GO ON

Directions: Read the passage and schedule, and answer the questions that follow.

Teresa's Busy October

1. Teresa has a busy October ahead of her. She has committed to attend a number of events at the Brovista Memorial Convention Center. Some of the events are on the same date.

2. Teresa would like to see her friend Kendra perform on the <u>didgeridoo</u> with the Outback Orchestra. She would also like to attend the second part of the Academic Achievement Series. In addition, her science teacher instructed her to go to the Observation Deck on the 19th. Most importantly, though, Teresa must attend the performance of *Leaves of Winter*, because she is a member of the play's cast.

3. With all of these obligations, Teresa wonders whether she will have any time to see anything else at the Convention Center.

Walter M. Brovista Memorial Convention Center
—October Schedule of Events—

Lectures and Seminars

Oct. 5, 3:00–5:00 P.M.	Academic Achievement Series, Part 2 Glen Maxey	Gallup Room
Oct. 11, 12:30–1:30 P.M.	Holistic Medicine Hal Dresser	Hancock Room
Oct. 12, 3:00–4:30 P.M.	Local Volunteer Opportunities Karen Francescoli	Hancock Room
Oct. 14, 6:30–8:00 P.M.	Introduction to Ceramics, Class 1 Megan Kearns	Hartley Studio
Oct. 19, 8:30–9:30 P.M.	The Fall Sky Margaret Davis	Observation Deck
Oct. 21, 6:30–8:00 P.M.	Introduction to Ceramics, Class 2 Megan Kearns	Hartley Studio

Fine Arts Productions*

Oct. 2, 8:00–9:30 P.M.	Tomlin Comedy Group	Bass Hall
Oct. 9, 6:30–8:00 P.M.	Hamlin Blue Grass Quartet	Toolson Stage
Oct. 12, 7:00–9:00 P.M.	Springfield Ballet	Bass Hall
Oct. 19, 2:45–5:00 P.M.	Outback Orchestra	Toolson Stage
Oct. 21, 7:00–8:30 P.M.	*Leaves in Winter*	Bass Hall
Oct. 30, 6:30–8:00 P.M.	Wayne Simpkins Dance Company	Bass Hall

* Tickets for each performance must be obtained at least three days before the event. <u>Patrons</u> should be advised that tickets do not guarantee seating.

25 Which fine art production performs first?
A Tomlin Comedy Group
B Hamlin Blue Grass Quartet
C Springfield Ballet
D Outback Orchestra

26 Teresa's science teacher *most* likely wanted her to—
F go to the Gallup Room on the 19th
G learn about volunteering in her neighborhood
H watch Wayne Simpkins dance
J see Margaret Davis's presentation

27 Which of the following is an *opinion* drawn from the schedule?
A The Springfield Ballet performs the same day that Karen Francescoli speaks.
B Convention Center events are poorly organized.
C Convention Center events take place in six locations.
D Kendra plays the didgeridoo.

28 Which heading in the passage provides additional information about tickets?
F Teresa's Busy October
G October Schedule of Events
H Lectures and Seminars
J Fine Arts Productions

29 If Teresa decides to take Introduction to Ceramics, Class 2, she will have to—
A miss Glen Maxey's lecture
B make special arrangements for October 14th
C bring clay to work with
D find someone to replace her in the play

30 If you wanted to find out how to pronounce the word <u>didgeridoo</u>, which of the following would be the *best* source?
F Encyclopedia
G Dictionary
H Internet
J Thesaurus

31 The *best* place for Teresa to keep track of the events she wants to attend is—
A an address book
B a piece of scrap paper
C a calendar
D a dictionary

32 Which event *probably* will present information about ways people can help their community?
F the performance by the Wayne Simpkins Dance Company
G the lecture on Local Volunteer Opportunities
H the Academic Achievement Series, Part 2 Seminar
J the seminar on Holistic Medicine

A Dream Within a Dream
Edgar Allan Poe

Take this kiss upon the brow!
And, in parting from you now,
Thus much let me avow—
You are not wrong, who deem
5   That my days have been a dream;
Yet if hope has flown away
In a night, or in a day,
In a vision, or in none,
Is it therefore the less *gone*?
10 *All* that we see or seem
Is but a dream within a dream.
I stand amid the roar
Of a surf-tormented shore,
And I hold within my hand
15 Grains of the golden sand—
How few! yet how they creep
Through my fingers to the deep,
While I weep—while I weep!
O God! can I not grasp
20 Them with a tighter clasp?
O God! can I not save
One from the pitiless wave?
Is *all* that we see or seem
But a dream within a dream?

---

33 What is hope like, based on these
lines: "Yet if hope has flown away / In
a night, or in a day"?
A Short-lived
B Steady
C Pointless
D Confusing

34 Lines 12–17 help the reader to—
F know what the beach is like
G realize that the speaker of the poem
cannot swim
H experience the same feelings as
the speaker
J understand that the poem is set
in summer

35 What is the conflict presented in the poem?

  A The speaker wants to learn to swim but cannot.

  B The speaker desperately wishes to hold on to the past.

  C The speaker has been losing sleep because of nightmares.

  D Time is passing quickly and the speaker feels rushed to finish work.

36 How does the speaker of this poem feel?

  F Sorrowful

  G Jealous

  H Bored

  J Indifferent

37 What happens in the first two lines of the poem?

  A The speaker goes to the sea.

  B Someone has a bad dream.

  C The speaker and his love part.

  D Day becomes night.

38 In lines 19–22, the speaker seems to be—

  F carrying something heavy

  G clinging to a ledge

  H rescuing someone from deep water

  J crying out for help

39 Lines 10–11 seem to say that—

  A some people have many dreams while they sleep

  B everyone has vision problems

  C life itself is like a dream

  D some dreams are sweet but others are not

40 The phrase "pitiless wave" gives the reader a sense of—

  F hopelessness

  G joy

  H accomplishment

  J peace

English: Writing

Directions: Read the passage in each shaded box. Read each question after the passage. Choose the best answer. Then mark the space on your answer sheet for the answer you have chosen.

SAMPLE A

> ### A Special Person
>
> In English class, Mark has been asked to write a description of a person who is special to him. Mark wants to write about his grandfather.

Which of these would *best* help Mark write his description of his grandfather?

A telling his friends about his grandfather

B thinking about all the things he likes about his grandfather

C making a list of all the things he will ask his grandfather when he sees him again

D asking his grandfather to take him to the library

SAMPLE B

> Here is the first part of Mark's rough draft.
>
> (1) A person who is special to me is my grandfather, his name is Randall Davis. (2) He lives in Norfolk, Virginia.

How should Sentence 1 be written?

F A person who is special to me is my grandfather, Randall Davis.

G A person who is special to me is my grandfather, but his name is Randall Davis.

H A person who is special to me is my grandfather, because his name is Randall Davis.

J A person who is special to me is my grandfather, although his name is Randall Davis.

SAMPLE C

> Here is the next part of Mark's rough draft.
>
> (3) <u>He tells</u> me stories about when he was a boy. (4) He listens as I tell him stories about home and school.

In Sentence 3, <u>He tells</u> should be written—

A He were telling

B He has telling

C He tell

D as it is

Falcons

Liz's English teacher has asked each student to write a short research essay on a topic of his or her choice.

1 Liz heard that peregrine falcons were once an endangered species but that they are not endangered anymore. She would like to write her essay about this topic. Which of these would *best* help Liz before she starts her research?

  A writing a rough draft of her essay

  B listing questions she has about her topic

  C asking her teacher if she likes falcons

  D rereading essays she has written in the past

2 Which of these books would *probably* provide Liz with the *most* useful information?

  F *How to Choose the Best Spots for Bird Watching*

  G *An Album of North American Birds*

  H *The Return of the Peregrine Falcon*

  J *How a Species Becomes Endangered*

Here is the first part of Liz's rough draft. Use it to answer questions 3–5.

(1) An adult peregrine falcon is between fifteen and twenty-two inches high and has long, pointed wings. (2) The birds have feathers that are white, tan, and dark brown when they are born. (3) When <u>they</u> turn two years old, they turn from dark brown to gray. (4) Peregrine falcons live in many parts of the world, including along the east coast of the United States. (5) For food, they usually eat other birds, attacking them in flight. (6) When the falcons lay eggs, there are usually four.

(7) In 1984, the peregrine falcon was listed as endangered. (8) Many of them did not survive a time in our country's history when a <u>certane</u> pesticide was used to prevent the spread of insects. (9) People did not know that the pesticide harmed animals such as the peregrine falcon. (10) When they found out about these effects, the pesticide no longer was used.

3 In Sentence 3, the first time the word <u>they</u> appears, it refers to—
A the falcons
B all the feathers
C the dark brown feathers
D the gray feathers

4 How is Sentence 6 *best* written?
F There are usually four when the falcons lay eggs.
G The falcons usually lay four eggs.
H When the falcons lay eggs, they usually lay four eggs.
J Four eggs are the number of eggs the falcons usually lay.

5 The correct spelling of <u>certane</u> in Sentence 8 is—
A certain
B sertain
C certene
D sertane

Read this next section of Liz's rough draft, and use it to answer questions 6–10. This section has groups of underlined words. The questions ask about these groups of underlined words.

(11) People in many states have helped the peregrine falcons that <u>survive</u>. (12) They have built cages on rooftops where the young birds are placed until they are ready to fly. (13) When the time comes, the <u>cages which are called hacking areas are left</u> open so that the falcons can come back anytime they want. (14) The birds learn to <u>fly strongly</u> and far.

(15) The falcons will live in the cages until they will stop coming back to the cages. (16) They will stay around cities sometimes. (17) They will also try to live near bodies of water such as rivers if <u>they</u> are available.

6 In Sentence 11, how is <u>survive</u> correctly written?
F will survive
G survives
H have survived
J as it is

7 In Sentence 13, how is <u>cages which are called hacking areas are left</u> correctly written?
A cages, which are called hacking areas, are left
B cages, which are called hacking areas are left
C cages which are called hacking areas, are left
D as it is

8 In Sentence 14, how is <u>fly strongly</u> correctly written?
F fly stronger
G fly strongest
H fly strong
J as it is

9 What needs to be changed in the second paragraph?
A It needs to have the same main idea as the first paragraph.
B It needs to also describe what the falcons look like.
C It needs to mention the endangered species list.
D It needs to have the same verb tense as the first paragraph.

10 In Sentence 17, to what noun does the second <u>they</u> refer?
F falcons
G cages
H bodies
J people

 GO ON

Read the two drafts of the first part of Lenny's letter. Use both drafts to answer questions 11–14.

DRAFT A

Dear Sixth Graders,

You may wonder how you can make your voice heard at Reed Middle School. I'm sure many of us students have great ideas about how we can make our school better and how we can solve problems when they happen. I hope that you will consider my invitation to join a special committee to help make a difference here at Reed. Each month, the committee will meet with Ms. Ellis and Mr. Kale.

We will begin by asking committee members to ask fellow students what they would like to change around school. You may hear about having more school social events or adding different items to the school lunch menu. Committee members will represent all of the sixth grade.

Meetings will take place right after school on the last Wednesday of each month. They will last a half hour or more, depending on how many ideas we have. Committee members will meet during lunch on the day of the meetings to decide who will talk about each idea.

GO ON

DRAFT B

Dear Sixth Graders,

Ms. Ellis, the principal here at Reed Middle School, has chosen me to form a committee that will meet with her and Mr. Kale once a month. They will listen to our ideas and concerns about student life here at Reed.

We will begin by asking committee members to ask fellow students what they would like to change around school. As you might imagine, having more school social events and offering new items on the lunch menu will likely be popular topics among our student body. Committee members will represent all of the sixth grade.

You might be wondering when the committee with meet with Ms. Ellis and Mr. Kale. Meetings will take place right after school on the last Wednesday of each month. They will last a half hour or more, depending on our plan. The committee will meet during lunch on the day of the meetings to assign roles to each member.

11 **The main difference between Paragraph 1 of Draft A and Paragraph 1 of Draft B is—**
  A Paragraph 1 of Draft A talks about what students can do if they had the chance
  B Paragraph 1 of Draft B uses a number of technical terms
  C Paragraph 1 of Draft A talks about when and where the committee will meet
  D Paragraph 1 of Draft B mentions the principal and vice principal

12 **Paragraph 2 of Draft A should be rewritten to—**
  F include more topics students will likely want to talk about
  G describe what Lenny will do as part of the committee
  H make it clear that "you" describes the committee members
  J describe what is wrong with the lunch menu

13 **Which of these could *best* be added at the end of Paragraph 3 in either draft?**
  A The committee will divide the duties based on what each member likes to do.
  B If committee members are absent, they must find someone to replace them at the meeting.
  C Ms. Ellis enjoys staying after school because it is much quieter and calmer then.
  D Some students ride the school bus and others walk home.

14 **How are the two drafts different in tone?**
  F In Draft A, it sounds as if Lenny doesn't think many people will join the committee.
  G In Draft A, it sounds as if Lenny wants to be the leader of the committee.
  H In Draft B, it sounds as if Lenny is angry.
  J In Draft B, Lenny's tone is more formal and serious.

Read this next section of Lenny's rough draft, and answer questions 15–19. This section has groups of underlined words. The questions ask about these groups of underlined words.

I <u>have schedule</u> a meeting for next Tuesday. If you are <u>interested in participated</u> on the committee, come to the library after school. Ms. Ellis will be there to answer your questions. Afterward, we can plan how we will split up the grade so that <u>they talk</u> to as many sixth graders as possible to find out what is important to students at Reed.

If you would like to help the sixth graders have more of a say in how our school is run, please plan to attend the meeting. If you would like to attend the meeting but know you cannot make it to the meeting on Tuesday, an information sheet and a permission form can be picked up; see me for <u>copies of it</u>. I am usually <u>found</u> outside the art room before school.

I hope many of you will join the committee.

Sincerely Yours,

Leonard Doyle

Leonard Doyle

---

15 How is <u>have schedule</u> correctly written?
A has schedule
B had scheduled
C have scheduled
D as it is

16 How is <u>interested in participated</u> correctly written?
F interest in participating
G interested in participating
H interesting in participating
J as it is

17 How is <u>they talk</u> correctly written?
A they talks
B we talk
C we talks
D as it is

18 How is <u>copies of it</u> correctly written?
F copies of them
G a copy of it
H copies of its
J as it is

19 How is <u>found</u> correctly written?
A find
B finds
C is found
D as it is

Direct Writing Component

In the direct writing component, students write a composition about a topic presented to them in a writing prompt. The writing prompt page also includes a "Checklist for Writers" that lists points for students to keep in mind as they write. Writing compositions are scored in each of the domains:

- Composing

- Written Expression

- Usage/Mechanics

Scores in the Composing and Written Expression domains are reported as part of the Reporting Category called **Plan, Compose, and Revise Writing in a Variety of Forms for a Variety of Purposes.** Scores in the Usage/Mechanics domains are reported as part of the Reporting Category called **Edit for Correct Use of Language, Capitalization, Punctuation, and Spelling.** A writing prompt appears on the following page.

English: Writing

PROMPT

Imagine that your local library will soon be adding something new. What do you think should be added? It may be a set of books, computer equipment, a book club, new shelves, or new furniture for library users. It might be something for children, adults, or both. Write to convince the library staff that your idea is the one that should be added. Be sure to be specific and explain your reasons.

CHECKLIST FOR WRITERS

____ I planned my paper before writing it.

____ I revised my paper to be sure that

    ____ the introduction captures the reader's attention;

    ____ the central idea is supported with specific information and examples that will be interesting to the reader;

    ____ the content relates to my central idea;

    ____ ideas are organized in a logical manner;

    ____ my sentences are varied in length;

    ____ my sentences are varied in the way that they begin; and

    ____ the conclusion brings my ideas together.

____ I edited my paper to be sure that

    ____ correct grammar is used;

    ____ words are capitalized when appropriate;

    ____ sentences are punctuated correctly;

    ____ words are spelled correctly; and

    ____ paragraphs are clearly indicated.

____ I checked my paper.

ITBS PRACTICE TEST

Vocabulary

DIRECTIONS

This is a test about words and their meanings.

■ For each question, you are to decide which one of the four answers has most nearly the same meaning as the underlined word above it.

■ Then, on your answer folder, find the row of answer spaces numbered the same as the question. Fill in the answer space that has the same letter as the answer you picked.

The sample on this page shows you what the questions are like and how to mark your answers.

SAMPLE

S1 To <u>embrace</u> a friend

   A find
   B hug
   C listen to
   D smile at

ANSWER

S1 A **B** C D

Vocabulary

1 A <u>clogged</u> drain

A blocked
B broken
C loose
D rusty

2 A freshly painted <u>exterior</u>

J building
K floor
L outside
M trimming

3 To <u>generate</u> responses

A display
B interpret
C grade
D produce

4 A <u>fictional</u> character

J cruel
K fascinating
L make-believe
M well-known

5 To <u>highlight</u> questions

A answer
B ask
C cancel
D stress

6 A <u>grouchy</u> dog

J crabby
K curious
L helpless
M watchful

7 Feeling <u>lightheaded</u>

A cranky
B dizzy
C happy
D sleepy

8 To <u>loathe</u> an enemy

J despise
K put up with
L scare
M talk to

9 A speedy <u>recovery</u>

A change
B completion
C healing
D trip

10 A different <u>aspect</u>

J feature
K file
L answer
M scene

11 A loud <u>clamor</u>

A ballad
B color
C machine
D racket

12 A <u>bewildering</u> action

J amusing
K annoying
L horrifying
M puzzling

13 A humble <u>abode</u>

A attitude
B home
C letter
D style

14 To <u>devise</u> a plan

J come up with
K put into action
L repeat
M take over

Reading Comprehension

DIRECTIONS

This is a test of how well you understand what you read.

- This test consists of reading passages followed by questions.

- Read each passage and then answer the questions.

- Four answers are given for each question. You are to choose the answer that you think is better than the others.

- Then, on your answer folder, find the row of answer spaces numbered the same as the question. Fill in the answer space for the best answer.

The sample on this page shows you what the questions are like and how to mark your answers.

SAMPLE

> As Lisa walked home from school, she thought about Mason and how sad he looked when Ms. Felter told him his science grade. "I should have helped him study," she said out loud. "He would have done that much for me." Lisa remembered all the times Mason had been there for her. When she had fallen off her bike, he had helped her up and brushed her off. When she had forgotten her lunch, he had given her half of his. He was the best friend anyone could ever have.

S1 **How does Lisa feel about Mason's science grade?**

A Angry
B Guilty
C Surprised
D Unconcerned

ANSWER

S1 A B C D

In "Childhood and Poetry," Pablo Neruda describes a memorable event from his youth. He is playing in his yard when a small, unidentified hand reaches through a hole in the fence and places a toy sheep on the ground. Years later, Neruda recalls how this exchange of gifts between strangers helped him give light to his poetry.

¶1   One time, investigating in the backyard of our house in Temuco the tiny objects and minuscule beings of my world, I came upon a hole in one of the boards of the fence. I looked through the hole and saw a landscape like that behind our house, uncared for, and wild. I moved back a few steps, because I sensed vaguely that something was about to happen. All of a sudden a hand appeared—a tiny hand of a boy about my own age. By the time I came close again, the hand was gone, and in its place there was a marvelous white sheep.

¶2   The sheep's wool was faded. Its wheels had escaped. All of this only made it more authentic. I had never seen such a wonderful sheep. I looked back through the hole but the boy had disappeared. I went into the house and brought out a treasure of my own: a pinecone, opened, full of odor and resin, which I adored. I set it down in the same spot and went off with the sheep.

¶3   I never saw either the hand or the boy again. And I have never again seen a sheep like that either. The toy I lost finally in a fire. But even now, in 1954, almost 50 years old, whenever I pass a toy shop, I look furtively into the window, but it's no use. They don't make sheep like that any more.

¶4   I have been a lucky man. To feel the intimacy of brothers is a marvelous thing in life. To feel the love of people whom we love is a fire that feeds our life. But to feel the affection that comes from those whom we do not know, from those unknown to us, who are watching over our sleep and solitude, over our dangers and our weaknesses—that is something still greater and more beautiful because it widens out the boundaries of our being, and unites all living things.

¶5   That exchange brought home to me for the first time a precious idea: that all of humanity is somehow together. That experience came to me again much later; this time it stood out strikingly against a background of trouble and persecution.

¶6   It won't surprise you then that I attempted to give something resiny, earthlike, and fragrant in exchange for human brotherhood. Just as I once left the pinecone by the fence, I have since left my words on the door of so many people who were unknown to me, people in prison, or hunted, or alone.

¶7   That is the great lesson I learned in my childhood, in the backyard of a lonely house. Maybe it was nothing but a game two boys played who didn't know each other and wanted to pass to the other some good things of life. Yet maybe this small and mysterious exchange of gifts remained inside me also, deep and indestructible, giving my poetry light.

1 Why did the little boy give the author the toy sheep?

   A He felt sorry for the author.
   B He wanted to be nice to the author.
   C The author had given him a pinecone.
   D The author had asked him for the sheep.

2 How does the author regard the toy sheep?

   J As earthlike
   K As intelligent
   L As precious
   M As threatening

3 In paragraph 6, what does the author mean when he says, "I have since left my words on the door of so many people"?

   A Many people have read his poetry.
   B He has sent letters to many people.
   C He has conversed with many people.
   D Many people have seen his drawings.

4 Which of these best describes the author's way of expressing himself?

   J He carefully describes an event exactly the way it happened.
   K He uses a simple childhood event to illustrate an important idea.
   L He uses persuasive language to convince the reader of his opinion.
   M He uses unbelievable exaggerations to let the reader know that he is telling a tall tale.

5 The author believes affection from people we don't know

   A is usually not welcome.
   B keeps us safe from danger.
   C unites us with all living things.
   D happens only during childhood.

6 In paragraph 7, what does "indestructible" mean?

   J Adjustable
   K Distinguishable
   L Incapable
   M Unbreakable

In this excerpt from the short story "Names/Nombres," Julia Alvarez recalls her family's early years as immigrants to the United States from the Dominican Republic. She describes how her family continually adjusted to the mispronunciation of their names.

¶1   When we arrived in New York City, our names changed almost immediately. At Immigration, the officer asked my father, *Mister Elbures,* if he had anything to declare. My father shook his head, "No," and we were waved through. I was too afraid we wouldn't be let in if I corrected the man's pronunciation, but I said our name to myself, opening my mouth wide for the organ blast of the *a,* trilling my tongue for the drumroll of the *r, All-vah-rrr-es!* How could anyone get *Elbures* out of that orchestra of sound?

¶2   At the hotel my mother was *Missus Alburest,* and I was *little girl,* as in, "Hey little girl, stop riding the elevator up and down. It's *not* a toy."

¶3   When we moved into our new apartment building, the super called my father *Mister Alberase,* and the neighbors who became mother's friends pronounced her name *Jew-lee-ah* instead of *Hoo-lee-ah.* I, her namesake, was known as *Hoo-lee-tah* at home. But at school, I was *Judy* or *Judith,* and once an English teacher mistook me for *Juliet.*

¶4   It took awhile to get used to my new names. I wondered if I shouldn't correct my teachers and new friends. But my mother argued that it didn't matter. "You know what your friend Shakespeare said, '*A rose by any other name would smell as sweet.*'" My father had gotten into the habit of calling any famous author "my friend" because I had begun to write poems and stories in English class.

7 When the people at the hotel called the author "little girl," they were

A giving her a nickname.
B hoping she would speak to them.
C speaking to her in a negative way.
D doing what her mother had told them do.

8 How did the author feel when her classmates called her *Judy* or *Judith?*

J Upset
K Ashamed
L Nervous
M Proud

9 In paragraph 4, what is meant by the quotation "A rose by any other name would smell as sweet"?

A Names are unimportant.
B People can live without names.
C A name is beautiful like a rose.
D The author's name is sweet like a rose.

10 In what way are famous authors Julia's "friends"?

J She is in classes with them at school.
K She reads their stories and poems.
L She also writes stories and poems.
M She is the top student in her English class.

In "Abuelito Who," by Sandra Cisneros, the speaker weaves earlier, happier impressions of her grandfather with her impressions of him as a frail man who "sleeps in his little room all night and day."

Abuelito[1] who throws coins like rain
and asks who loves him
who is dough and feathers
who is a watch and glass of water
whose hair is made of fur
is too sad to come downstairs today
who tells me in Spanish you are my
diamond
who tells me in English you are my sky
whose little eyes are string
can't come out to play
sleeps in his little room all night and day
who used to laugh like the letter k
is sick
is a doorknob tied to a sour stick
is tired shut the door
doesn't live here anymore
is hiding underneath the bed
who talks to me inside my head
is blankets and spoons and big brown
shoes
who snores up and down up and down
up and down again
is the rain on the roof that falls like coins
asking who loves him
who loves him who?

[1]**Abuelito** (ä bwe lē′ tō): In Spanish, an affectionate term for a grandfather.

11 **When the author says her grandfather "talks to me inside my head," she means**

A she is thinking about him.
B he is whispering in her ear.
C she has troubling hearing him.
D her mother is talking about him.

12 **How does the speaker of the poem feel about her grandfather?**

J Angry
K Confused
L Nervous
M Thrilled

13 **What does the speaker mean in the last line of the poem?**

A Her grandfather is in a hospital.
B She does not love her grandfather.
C She has never seen her grandfather.
D She no longer recognizes her grandfather.

14 **When the speaker says her grandfather is "dough and feathers" she means he is**

J large.
K soft.
L thin.
M warm.

Spelling

DIRECTIONS

This test will show how well you can spell.

■ Many of the questions in this test contain mistakes in spelling. Some do not have any mistakes at all.

■ You should look for mistakes in spelling.

■ When you find a mistake, fill in the answer space on your answer folder that has the same letter as the **line** containing the mistake.

■ If there is no mistake, fill in the last answer space.

The samples on this page show you what the questions are like and how to mark your answers.

SAMPLES

S1
- **A** explane
- **B** hornet
- **C** brilliance
- **D** devote
- **E** *(No mistakes)*

S2
- **J** hopeless
- **K** parcel
- **L** radar
- **M** repair
- **N** *(No mistakes)*

ANSWERS
S1 **A** B C D E
S2 J K L M **N**

Spelling

1
- A harmful
- B greatful
- C healthful
- D playful
- E *(No mistakes)*

2
- J clamor
- K docter
- L flounder
- M sailor
- N *(No mistakes)*

3
- A hoarse
- B cinch
- C ought
- D drought
- E *(No mistakes)*

4
- J plague
- K leegue
- L earn
- M turn
- N *(No mistakes)*

5
- A impresion
- B infection
- C reflection
- D inscription
- E *(No mistakes)*

6
- J protector
- K encountor
- L deliver
- M producer
- N *(No mistakes)*

7
- A amazement
- B element
- C improvment
- D refreshment
- E *(No mistakes)*

8
- J diagram
- K absolute
- L buttermilk
- M canary
- N *(No mistakes)*

9
- A deliteful
- B forgetful
- C regretful
- D plentiful
- E *(No mistakes)*

10
- J gourmet
- K bouquet
- L context
- M afflict
- N *(No mistakes)*

11
- A detergent
- B principal
- C accompliss
- D computer
- E *(No mistakes)*

12
- J dwarf
- K moose
- L ounce
- M raise
- N *(No mistakes)*

13
- A reaction
- B election
- C collection
- D atraction
- E *(No mistakes)*

14
- J feilder
- K welder
- L flutter
- M glitter
- N *(No mistakes)*

Capitalization

DIRECTIONS

This is a test on capitalization. It will show how well you can use capital letters in sentences.

■ You should look for mistakes in capitalization in the sentences on this test.

■ When you find a mistake, fill in the answer space on your answer folder that has the same letter as the **line** containing the mistake.

■ Some sentences do not have any mistakes at all. If there is no mistake, fill in the last answer space.

The samples on this page show you what the questions are like and how to mark your answers.

SAMPLES

S1 A Anne Tyler, the author
    B of *Breathing lessons,* is one
    C of my all-time favorite writers.
    D *(No mistakes)*

S2 J Kristina's father bought
    K her a new blue Convertible
    L for her sixteenth birthday.
    M *(No mistakes)*

S3 A If you ever visit Norway, be
    B sure to see the ancient ships
    C kept in the museums.
    D *(No mistakes)*

ANSWERS

S1 A **B** C D

S2 J **K** L M

S3 A B C **D**

Capitalization

1
A My teacher rolled his eyes
B and said, "please don't tell me
C the dog ate your homework."
D *(No mistakes)*

2
J A Tanager is a beautiful, colorful
K bird that is very common in the
L Southwest and in southern
California.
M *(No mistakes)*

3
A "Would you be kind enough to carry
B this great big suitcase for me?" the sweet
C old woman asked the worried little boy.
D *(No mistakes)*

4
J Last winter we visited aunt Carrie
K in Mesa, Arizona, where
L she owns a small summer home.
M *(No mistakes)*

5
A *The Horse whisperer,* a novel by
B Nicholas Evans, about a man who talks
C to horses, is set in Montana.
D *(No mistakes)*

6
J Jamie lives West of our
K house, on Hamilton Street, in
L a town called Wyoming.
M *(No mistakes)*

7
A In the late 1800s, the Brontë
B Sisters published novels under the
C names Currier, Ellis, and Acton Bell.
D *(No mistakes)*

8
J 155 Hightop Drive, Apt. 4
K Binghamton, NY
L September 27, 2001
M *(No mistakes)*

9
A Dr. Carol Harris
B Riverview college
C Dear Dr. Harris:
D *(No mistakes)*

10
J I am writing this letter to tell you how
K much I enjoyed your book, *Planetary Wonders.*
L I particularly enjoyed the chapter about mars.
M *(No mistakes)*

11
A I would also like to ask you if I may
B photocopy chapter 9 for an oral presentation
C I am giving on the solar system.
D *(No mistakes)*

12
J I'm in the sixth grade at Montgomery Elementary.
K Sincerely yours,
L Charles Moyerowski
M *(No mistakes)*

13
A My sister Cara is a successful
B photographer who worked her way
C through College and supported me as well.
D *(No mistakes)*

Punctuation

DIRECTIONS

This is a test on punctuation. It will show how well you can use periods, question marks, commas, and other kinds of punctuation marks.

■ You should look for mistakes in punctuation in the sentences on this test.

■ When you find a mistake, fill in the answer space on your answer folder that has the same letter as the **line** containing the mistake.

■ Some sentences do not have any mistakes at all. If there is no mistake, fill in the last answer space.

The samples on this page show you what the questions are like and how to mark your answers.

SAMPLES

S1
A The three girls earned the
B money for the trip by baby-sitting
C and saving their allowances.
D *(No mistakes)*

S2
J Because of the upcoming
K snowstorm school was
L dismissed at noon today.
M *(No mistakes)*

S3
A The dog liked three things
B best, running in the field,
C chasing the ball, and eating.
D *(No mistakes)*

ANSWERS

S1 A B C **D**
S2 J **K** L M
S3 A **B** C D

Punctuation

1   A   The Norway Spruce an evergreen
    B   tree, was brought to the United
    C   States from Europe.
    D   *(No mistakes)*

2   J   On December 10 1949 the
    K   AAFC and NFL merged and made
    L   the Cleveland Browns part of the
       NFL.
    M   *(No mistakes)*

3   A   Sara knew her little sister wasn't
       telling
    B   the truth because she rolled her
       eyes and
    C   said "Give me a break already,
       will you?"
    D   *(No mistakes)*

4   J   Even though Arthur Harris earned
       straight
    K   A's since the first grade, each time
       he took a
    L   test he asked the teacher, "How
       did I do."
    M   *(No mistakes)*

5   A   My 71-year-old mother writes
       novels,
    B   paints pictures, sings in the
    C   choir, and is a devout baseball
       fan.
    D   *(No mistakes)*

6   J   The clavicle is a long thin bone
    K   located at the root of the neck.
       Just below
    L   the skin in front of the first rib.
    M   *(No mistakes)*

7   A   Michelangelo who spent his life
    B   in Florence and Rome, was a
       talented
    C   painter, sculptor, poet, and
       architect.
    D   *(No mistakes)*

8   J   Brackton Middle School
    K   Brackton, PA 18641
    L   January 10 2000
    M   *(No mistakes)*

9   A   Dear Friend:
    B   The students at Brackton
       Area Middle School are
    C   holding the annual
       Valentine's Day dance on
       February 14.
    D   *(No mistakes)*

10   J   Would you consider
       donating party supplies
     K   for the dance. The proceeds
       from ticket sales
     L   to the dance will benefit local
       charities.
     M   *(No mistakes)*

11   A   Thank you for your
       consideration.
     B   Sincerely,
     C   The Students at
       Brackton Middle
       School
     D   *(No mistakes)*

12   J   Because of rising airline costs
     K   many people are choosing to drive
     L   to vacation spots instead of flying.
     M   *(No mistakes)*

Usage and Expression

DIRECTIONS

This is a test on the use of words. It will show how well you can use words according to the standards of correctly written English.

■ You should look for mistakes in the sentences on this test.

■ When you find a mistake, fill in the answer space on your answer folder that has the same letter as the **line** containing the mistake.

■ Some sentences do not have any mistakes at all. If there is no mistake, fill in the last answer space.

The samples on this page show you what the questions are like and how to mark your answers.

SAMPLES

S1 A When it comes to science, both of
     B my favorite teachers, Mrs. Keton and
     C Ms. Connelly, knows her stuff.
     D *(No mistakes)*

S2 J Ernest Hemingway was a
     K famous writer who living in a mansion
     L in Key West with over 60 cats.
     M *(No mistakes)*

ANSWERS

S1 A B **C** D

S2 J **K** L M

Usage

1
A   Each of the girls knows the
B   combination to their locker as well
C   as her identification number.
D   *(No mistakes)*

2
J   Stephen King, a famous horror
K   writer, usually writing his
    novels in
L   the basement of his home.
M   *(No mistakes)*

3
A   Shelby said she don't have no idea
B   why her brother didn't show
    up for
C   band practice last Tuesday.
D   *(No mistakes)*

4
J   A cat named Shade McCorkle
K   once saved his owner's life
L   by fending off an intruder.
M   *(No mistakes)*

5
A   Most physicians agree that, in
B   addition to improving your muscle
C   tone, exercise can lifting your
    spirits.
D   *(No mistakes)*

6
J   Some people believe that e-mail
    will
K   eventually replace mail as the
    primary
L   means of written correspondence.
M   *(No mistakes)*

7
A   After scuba diving for three
B   days, we found the rare puffer
    fish,
C   just what we was looking for.
D   *(No mistakes)*

8
J   A recent survey showed that many
K   Americans don't realize that 220
L   is a high cholesterol level.
M   *(No mistakes)*

9
A   My mother's store of
B   patience is great, but my father's
C   is even more greater.
D   *(No mistakes)*

10
J   For all their power, the human
K   heart is amazingly small—about
L   the size of two fists.
M   *(No mistakes)*

Expression

DIRECTIONS

This is Part 2 of the test about the use of words. It will show how well you can express ideas correctly and effectively. There are several sections to this part of the test. Read the directions to each section carefully. Then mark your answers on your answer folder.

Directions: Use this paragraph to answer questions 11–14.

> [1]The *Tyrannosaurus Rex*, or T-Rex as it is commonly called, was a gigantic dinosaur that roamed North America more than 70 million years ago. [2]Its head was more than 4 feet long, and some of its teeth were larger than a human hand. [3]T-Rex stood about 19 feet high and was <u>pretty close to</u> 47 feet long. [4]Its massive tail was probably used to balance its heavy head. [5]Dimetrodon was the most common meat-eating dinosaur and lived in Permian times, almost 260 million years ago.

11 Which is the best place for sentence 2?

  A Where it is now
  B Before Sentence 1
  C Between Sentences 3 and 4
  D After Sentence 5

12 Which sentence should be left out of this paragraph?

  J Sentence 1
  K Sentence 2
  L Sentence 4
  M Sentence 5

13 Which is the best way to rewrite the underlined part of sentence 3?

  A about
  B probably almost
  C somewhere around
  D *(No change)*

14 Which is the best concluding sentence for this paragraph?

  J Scientists are still unsure what happened to T-Rex that made it become extinct.
  K Although the T-Rex was massive, it was not as feared as the Velociraptor, a smaller dinosaur that hunted in packs.
  L The T-Rex has been featured in many movies, some of them enormously popular.
  M Scientists believe T-Rex mothers were extremely protective of their young.

Directions: In questions 15–16, choose the best way to
express the idea.

15 A Many experts believe that a fear of public speaking can be conquered with practice.
   B With practice, a fear of public speaking can be conquered, many experts believe.
   C A belief held by many experts is that a fear of public speaking can be conquered
      with practice.
   D That a fear of public speaking can be conquered with a practice, is a belief held by
      many experts.

16 J The gray squirrel is common in the North, but frequently raids bird feeders and
      garbage cans.
   K The gray squirrel, which is common in the North, frequently raids bird feeders and
      garbage cans.
   L While the gray squirrel is common in the North, it frequently raids bird feeders and
      garbage cans.
   M A frequent raider of bird feeders and garbage cans is the gray squirrel that's
      common in the North.

Directions: In questions 17–19, choose the best way to write
the underlined part of the sentence.

17 My little sister Kelsy likes to sing, _dancing_, and play the piano.
   A will dance   **B** dance   **C** to dance   **D** *(No change)*

18 I should _have went_ to the game, instead of just watching television all evening.
   J have gone   **K** had went   **L** going   **M** *(No change)*

19 Which of these would be most persuasive in a letter to the school board?

   A We students feel the new mandatory community service requirement for all graduating seniors is unfair. Many of us have after-school jobs and can't spare 10 hours a month. In addition, some of our parents can't provide us with the necessary transportation to and from the service facility we are assigned.

   B Some of us seniors don't like the new mandatory community service requirement. Making us serve the community in order to graduate isn't fair. We want to spend our time in other ways. How can we find time to study and serve the community? Please reconsider this requirement.

   C We're attending this meeting to try to persuade you to change the new mandatory community service requirement. You're forcing us to do something we may not want to do.

   D The new community service requirement is completely unfair. Seniors don't want to do this. We need to spend time with our friends. We have a petition with us. Basically, we refuse to do this.

TERRANOVA PRACTICE TEST

Reading and Language Arts

Sample Passage

Respect

People from various cultures have different ways of showing respect toward one another. In some cultures people shake hands upon meeting. In others, people hug each other as a way of greeting. In the United States, eye contact is encouraged, but in some cultures, eye contact is a sign of rudeness.

Sample A

This passage is mostly about

Ⓐ how people show respect

Ⓑ how people shake hands

Ⓒ why eye contact is rude

Ⓓ why greetings are important

Directions

A student wrote a paragraph about his older brother. There are some mistakes that need correcting.

---

[1]For as long as I can remember, my older brother Mark has been there. [2]Mark has always been there for me. [3]He taught me how to have faith in myself and to stand up for what I believe in. [4]I always knew that whenever I had a problem, Mark would be there for me, trying to make things better.

Sample B

Which of these best combines Sentences 1 and 2?

Ⓕ For as long as I can remember, my older brother Mark has been there for me.

Ⓖ My older brother Mark, for as long as I can remember, has been there for me.

Ⓗ Because my older brother Mark has been there, for as long as I can remember.

Ⓙ My older brother Mark has always been there for me, at least as long as I can remember.

Sample C

Where would this sentence best fit into the paragraph?

I know he'll also be there for me in the future.

Ⓐ after Sentence 1

Ⓑ after Sentence 2

Ⓒ after Sentence 3

Ⓓ after Sentence 4

Far-Away Places

Have you ever visited a far-away place? Many people travel to different places on vacations or to visit friends and family. Visiting someplace that's very different from your home can be a great learning experience—and a lot of fun.

In this theme you'll read about some people who have visited some fascinating places, and you'll have a chance to write about a place you would like to visit. Start Reading and begin learning about **Far-Away Places.**

The Loch Ness Monster *by* George Laycock

Directions

Each year, tourists flock to Loch Ness, Scotland, in the hopes of catching a glimpse of Nessie, the famous Loch Ness monster. While many doubt that the monster actually exists, in this excerpt from "The Loch Ness Monster," George Laycock discusses why researchers are beginning to believe that Nessie may be real after all. Read the excerpt. Then, do Numbers 1 through 6.

In 1938, a tugboat captain was steering his boat across Loch Ness. Everything seemed to be in order. The sky was cloudy just as it is much of the time around Loch Ness. The water was rough from the wind. The tug plowed on mile after mile, its engines laboring normally. The captain was not thinking about monsters. He didn't believe in Nessie anyhow. He made this plain enough to anyone who asked him if he'd ever seen the beast. Then beside the boat, a creature like nothing the captain had ever seen before stuck its long humped back out of the water. It had a long, slender neck and a little head. The monster rushed ahead, gained speed on the tug, and disappeared far out in front of the boat. This was enough to change the captain's mind. As far as he was concerned, Nessie was real, after all.

Other sightings even included an observation by a driver who saw Nessie in the beam of his headlights on a dark night as the monster crossed the highway near the loch.

These stories were told and retold. Word of Nessie spread around the world. This did a marvelous thing for Scotland. Tourists began to visit Loch Ness, hoping for a glimpse of the elusive lake monster. Tourism can be good for a country's economy. Nessie, real or not, became the most valuable animal in all Scotland.

But the lecturer who was to tell us about the Loch Ness monster that night in Oxford, Ohio, had brought scientific methods to the search for Nessie, and people were eager to hear his message. All the seats were filled and students stood around the walls and sat in the aisles to listen to the story Robert H. Rines had to tell.

Dr. Rines, president of the Boston Academy of Applied Science, led his first scientific expedition to Loch Ness in 1970. He took along modern sonar equipment and used this to "see" into the murky depths. Sonar works by sending high-intensity sound impulses into the water and measuring the echoes sent back as the sound waves bounce off the bottom or off objects between it and the bottom. It can reveal the depth of objects in the water, their size, and whether or not they are moving. That summer the sonar equipment showed the researchers important facts. There were large moving objects in the loch. Also there were abundant fish to feed monsters.

Dr. Rines meanwhile was consulting with his colleagues, searching for still better equipment for gathering information about the monster of Loch Ness. He worked with Dr. Harold E. Edgerton, who, as a professor at Massachusetts Institute of Technology, had pioneered in the development of high-speed underwater photography. Dr. Edgerton had also developed remarkable strobe lights for making pictures in dingy water. Now, he designed a system of lights Dr. Rines might use to obtain closeup pictures in Loch Ness.

Dr. Rines linked his camera to the sonar and set it so that it would begin making pictures automatically as soon as any large object passed through the sonar field. It would continue to make pictures every fifteen seconds as long as the sonar told it to.

For their first test, the crew of monster seekers chose the bay where Nessie had most often been sighted. They carefully cleaned the camera lens, then began lowering it gently toward the lake bottom. Divers checked it

there and found it clean and ready to make monster pictures.

Another camera was suspended under the research boat and pointed downward into the dark water. All that was needed now was to wait for Nessie to come nosing around.

But a strange thing happened. The lens of the camera on the bottom of the loch was suddenly covered with sand, apparently kicked onto it by some large frightened creature. Had Nessie been there and kicked up the silt?

That camera, with its sand-covered lens, made no pictures. But the other camera, hanging beneath the boat, was still in working order. It yielded pictures that to some looked plainly like parts of a huge unknown monster swimming in the water. These color pictures were perhaps the best evidence that there really is a Nessie.

1 **Choose the sentence that best describes what the passage is mostly about.**

Ⓐ The Loch Ness monster may actually be a large water reptile.

Ⓑ New evidence is convincing more people that the Loch Ness monster is real.

Ⓒ A tugboat captain recounts seeing the Loch Ness monster swim past his boat.

Ⓓ Some scientists refuse to believe in the Loch Ness monster, in spite of evidence that it may be real.

2 **According to the passage, while Dr. Rines was using sonar to "see" the depths of the Loch, he was also "consulting with his colleagues, searching for still better equipment." The word *colleagues* probably means**

Ⓕ employees

Ⓖ neighbors

Ⓗ peers

Ⓙ supplies

3 **Which of these best describes Dr. Rines?**

Ⓐ content

Ⓑ disappointed

Ⓒ nervous

Ⓓ hopeful

4 The answer you chose for Number 3 is best because you learned from the passage that

Ⓕ Dr. Rines was unable to prove that the monster exists.

Ⓖ Dr. Rines gathered evidence that may prove the monster is real.

Ⓗ Dr. Rines was worried that the monster would damage his sonar equipment.

Ⓙ Dr. Rines believed that he had gathered enough evidence to prove that the monster is real.

5 Stories of the Loch Ness monster were good for Scotland because

Ⓐ scientists visited the loch to gather research

Ⓑ students visited the loch to study the monster

Ⓒ tourists visited the loch hoping to see the monster

Ⓓ fisherman visited the loch hoping to catch the monster

6 In the passage, the author says that people "began to visit Loch Ness, hoping for a glimpse of the elusive lake monster." The word *elusive* probably means

Ⓕ aggressive

Ⓖ huge

Ⓗ shy

Ⓙ strange

Directions

Ms. Chan's class is writing about places they have visited or places they would like to visit. Carol wrote about a visit to see her aunt and uncle in Ocean City, Maryland. Here is her essay. There are several mistakes that need correcting.

---

¹Last summer, my Aunt Deeny and Uncle Phil invited my brother Marc and me to spend two weeks with them at their home in Ocean City, Maryland. ²Marc and I live in Ohio, we had never been to the ocean, so we were very excited. ³Aunt Deeny and Uncle Phil live in a house that's next to a beautiful bay. ⁴They have a dock in the back of the house, so they can driving their boat right up to their back door. ⁵Marc and I spent most of our days at the beach, which is beautiful. ⁶The beach is very crowded in the summer. ⁷Uncle Phil taught Marc and I to learn how to bodyboard. ⁸You put the bodyboard underneath your stomach and glide on the waves. ⁹We weren't very good at it when we first tried it. ¹⁰I scraped my arms and swallowed some sea water. ¹¹However, by the end of the trip, we was very good. ¹²Even though the beach was a blast, the best part of the trip was spending time with Aunt Deeny and Uncle Phil. ¹³I hope we can visit them again next summer.

---

7 Which sentence contains two complete thoughts and should be written as two sentences?

Ⓐ Sentence 1

Ⓑ Sentence 2

Ⓒ Sentence 11

Ⓓ Sentence 12

8 The best way to write Sentence 4 is

Ⓕ In the back of their house, they have a dock so they drive their boat right up to the back.

Ⓖ They have a dock in the back of the house, so they can drive their boat right up to their back door.

Ⓗ They will drive their boat right up to the back door, because they have a dock in the back of the house.

Ⓙ Best as it is

9 **Which of these best combines Sentences 5 and 6?**

    Ⓐ Marc and I spent most of our days at the beach, which is beautiful and very crowded in the summer.

    Ⓑ Marc and I spent most of our days at the beautiful beach, which is also very crowded in the summer.

    Ⓒ The beach is beautiful in the summer and very crowded, but Marc and I spent most of our days there.

    Ⓓ The beach is very crowded in the summer and Marc and I spent most of our days at the beach, which is beautiful.

10 **Which is the best way to write Sentence 7?**

    Ⓕ Uncle Phil taught Marc and me how to bodyboard.

    Ⓖ Marc and I were taught by Uncle Phil how to bodyboard.

    Ⓗ Marc and I learned how to bodyboard from Uncle Phil, who taught us.

    Ⓙ Best as it is

11 **Choose the best way to write Sentence 11.**

    Ⓐ We was very good by the end of the trip, however.

    Ⓑ When the trip ended, we were very good, however.

    Ⓒ However, by the end of the trip, we were very good.

    Ⓓ Best as it is

12 **Where would this sentence best fit in the paragraph?**

A bodyboard looks like a small surfboard.

    Ⓕ after Sentence 7

    Ⓖ after Sentence 8

    Ⓗ after Sentence 9

    Ⓙ after Sentence 10

An Astronaut's Answers *by* John Glenn

Directions

In this interview, John Glenn answers questions about what it's like to travel in space. John Glenn was the first American to travel around the Earth in space, on February 20, 1962. He orbited the Earth three times in the spacecraft *Friendship* 7. Thirty-six years later at age 77, on board the shuttle *Discovery*, he became the oldest person ever to travel in space. Read the interview. Then, do numbers 13 to 18.

The first time you went into space, how did it feel to be all alone except for communication through radio?

In 1962, I looked down from an orbit high above our planet and saw our beautiful Earth and its curved horizon against the vastness of space. I have never forgotten that sight nor the sense of wonder it engendered. Although I was alone in *Friendship 7,* I did not feel alone in space. I knew that I was supported by my family, my six fellow astronauts, thousands of NASA engineers and employees, and millions of people around the world.

Why did you want to be an astronaut? How did you fly around the Earth three times? Was it hard?

I served as a fighter pilot in World War II and the Korean conflict. After Korea, I graduated from the Naval Test Pilot School and worked as a fighter test pilot. I applied for the astronaut program because I thought it was a logical career step, a challenging opportunity and one in which I could help start a new area of research that would be very valuable to everyone here and on Earth. I have always considered myself very fortunate to be selected in the first group of seven astronauts.

An Atlas rocket boosted me into space and I orbited the Earth in my space capsule, the *Friendship 7.* It certainly was a challenge but one for which I was well prepared. The National Aeronautics and Space Administration (NASA) wanted people who were test pilots and accustomed to working under very unusual conditions, including emergencies. During my first orbit, I experienced some troubles with the automatic control system and so I had to take control of the capsule's movements by hand for the rest of the trip. Another problem developed when the signals showed that the head shield was loose. To keep it secured during re-entry, I kept the retrorocket pack in place to steady the shield. When the *Friendship 7* entered the atmosphere, the retrorocket pack burned off and flew by the window, but the head shield stayed in place. These were problems we could not have foreseen prior to the flight.

How long was your trip around the Earth?

My trip around the Earth lasted 4 hours and 55 minutes, and I flew about 81,000 miles.

What did you eat while you were in outer space?

I took along a number of different kinds of food, such as applesauce and a mixture of meat and vegetables, all emulsified like baby food. It was packaged in containers much like toothpaste tubes so I could squeeze food into my mouth. I had no trouble eating any of it and it tasted fine.

Why do astronauts go to the moon?

As adventurers of earlier eras crossed oceans and scaled mountains, astronauts in our time have flown to the moon and explored the heavens. The crucial hands-on experience of my flight in the Mercury program helped make the Gemini flights possible. The Gemini flights then helped make the Apollo missions to the moon a reality. Apollo gave us valuable information for the Shuttle missions, and the Shuttle/Mir program prepares us for the International

Space Station. This is the nature of progress. Each of the missions has built on the knowledge gained from the previous flights.

We are a curious, questing people and our research in this new laboratory of space represents an opportunity to benefit people right here on Earth and to increase our understanding of the universe. The potential scientific, medical, and economic benefits from space are beyond our wildest dreams. That's why astronauts went to the moon, and that's why we continue to pursue our dreams of space exploration.

13 **The interview you have just read is mostly about**

Ⓐ an astronaut's thoughts on space travel

Ⓑ an astronaut's eating habits

Ⓒ how people train to become astronauts

Ⓓ how astronauts survive in spacecraft

14 **John Glenn trained to become an astronaut by**

Ⓕ building spacecraft

Ⓖ studying space in college

Ⓗ working as a fighter pilot

Ⓙ working as a NASA engineer

15 **According to the interview, why do astronauts travel to the moon?**

Ⓐ to gain knowledge

Ⓑ to cross the oceans

Ⓒ to prepare for the future

Ⓓ to prove that it can be done

16 **Which of these was probably the hardest part of John Glenn's first time around the earth?**

Ⓕ being alone

Ⓖ eating food in tubes

Ⓗ surviving bad weather conditions

Ⓙ dealing with mechanical difficulties

17 **The author's purpose for writing this article was probably to report on John Glenn's**

Ⓐ experiences in space

Ⓑ dreams for the future

Ⓒ discoveries of unknown lands

Ⓓ beliefs about the space program

18 **Here are two sentences related to the passage.**

John Glenn traveled in space aboard the space shuttle Discovery. *He was 77 years old.*

Which of these best combines the two sentences into one?

Ⓕ He was 77 years old, but John Glenn traveled in space aboard the space shuttle *Discovery.*

Ⓖ When he was 77 years old, John Glenn traveled in space aboard the space shuttle *Discovery.*

Ⓗ While John Glenn traveled in space aboard the space shuttle *Discovery,* he was 77 years old.

Ⓙ John Glenn traveled in space aboard the space shuttle *Discovery,* and he was 77 years old.

Let's Write

Sample D

There are <u>four</u> mistakes in this paragraph. Let's correct them together.

> Last winter, my friend Clara asking me to go on a three-day skiing trip with her. It sounded like fun, but skiing is more harder than you would think. I couldn't even stand the first day. I fell off the ski lift. I felled all the way down the bunny slope. I lost one of my poles in the Woods. I crashed into a fence. Eventually, however, I got the hang of it. I'm still not a great skier, but I have mastered the bunny slope.

19 **A student wrote this paragraph about imaginary trips he takes while camping outdoors with his brother. There are <u>five</u> mistakes in the paragraph. Draw a line through each part that has a mistake, and write the correction above it.**

> In the summer my older brother Matt and me sleep in a tent in our backyard. Sometimes we pretending the tent is a space ship that takes us to all kinds of places. Every now and then, we go to the moon in our space ship, although once I fell in a crater and hurted my knee. Other times, we travel from star to star in the ship, and sometimes we stop at a planet to get a bite to eat. Matt can even make our space ship travel back in time, once we pretended we were Cowboys riding our horses across the Great Plains. We never know quite where we'll end up.

Directions

Study this poster encouraging students to attend a ski trip.

The Middle View Area Ski Club will hold a

Ski Trip to Camelback Ski Resort

on January 10

Students, friends, and family of all ages welcome!

Bus leaves the school at 8:30 A.M. and returns at 10:30 P.M.

Cost is $45 a person, including ski rental, lunch, and dinner.

Tickets available at the school office.

The Ski Club needs your help! Students and parents need to
organize and supervise the trip.

Call Tony Parks at 555-234-8897 for more information.

---

20 **Now use the information from the poster to do the following:**

Write the information that is most important if you plan to attend the ski trip.

_____

Write the information that is most important if you want to help with the trip.

_____

Write one phrase from the poster that is meant to persuade you to help.

_____

21 Look back at the excerpt from "The Loch Ness Monster." Now think about John
Glenn's experience in outer space. If you could travel to any place in the universe,
where would you go and why? What would you do on your trip? Write a paragraph
discussing your answer.

For this answer, be sure to use complete sentences and check your work for correct
spelling, capitalization, and punctuation.

_____

_____

_____

_____

_____

_____

_____

_____

SAT 10 PRACTICE TEST

Vocabulary

Directions:

Look at each underlined word. Choose the word that means about the same thing.

1 To <u>supervise</u> is to—

   A lose

   B win

   C argue

   D oversee

2 Something that is <u>vacant</u> is—

   F noisy

   G empty

   H round

   J nearby

3 <u>Mobility</u> refers to—

   A motion

   B speed

   C distance

   D height

4 <u>Accurately</u> means—

   F purposely

   G correctly

   H quickly

   J recently

Directions:

Read each boxed sentence. Then, read the sentences that follow. Choose the sentence that uses the underlined word in the same way as in the box.

5

> <u>Kick</u> the ball into the goal.

In which sentence does the word <u>kick</u> mean the same thing as in the sentence above?

   A Janet got a <u>kick</u> out of the comedy show.

   B Please don't <u>kick</u> me out of the club.

   C Barney should <u>kick</u> the habit of oversleeping.

   D It is mean to <u>kick</u> other people.

6

> The tree branches <u>shake</u>.

In which sentence does the word <u>shake</u> mean the same thing as in the sentence above?

   F Boris drank a chocolate milk <u>shake</u>.

   G His hand<u>shake</u> was very strong.

   H I can't <u>shake</u> the cold I've had all week.

   J The baby likes to <u>shake</u> the rattle.

Reading Comprehension

from "Names/Nombres" by Julia Alvarez

Directions:

Read this excerpt from "Names/Nombres" by Julia Alvarez. Then, complete numbers 1 through 4 by choosing the best answer.

When we arrived in New York City, our names changed almost immediately. At Immigration, the officer asked my father, *Mister Elbures*, if he had anything to declare. My father shook his head, "No," and we were waved through. I was too afraid we wouldn't be let in if I corrected the man's pronunciation, but I said our name to myself, opening my mouth wide for the organ blast of the *a*, trilling my tongue for the drum-roll of the *r*, *All-vah-rrr-es!* How could anyone get *Elbures* out of that orchestra of sound?

At the hotel my mother was *Missus Alburest*, and I was little girl, as in, "Hey *little girl*, stop riding the elevator up and down. It's *not* a toy."

When we moved into our new apartment building, the super [the apartment manager] called my father *Mister Alberase*, and the neighbors who became mother's friends pronounced her name *Jew-lee-ah* instead of *Hoo-lee-ah*. I, her namesake, was known as *Hoo-lee-tah* at home. But at school, I was *Judy* or *Judith*, and once an English teacher mistook me for *Juliet*.

It took awhile to get used to my new names. I wondered if I shouldn't correct my teachers and new friends. But my mother argued that it didn't matter. "You know what your friend Shakespeare said, *'A rose by any other name would smell as sweet.'*" My father had gotten into the habit of calling any famous author "my friend" because I had begun to write poems and stories in English class.

1 Why was the author called by so many different names?

  A Americans had trouble saying her name.

  B She changed her name often in school.

  C Her teachers frequently mispronounced her name.

  D Her parents called her by different names.

2 The author's mother quotes Shakespeare: "A rose by any other name would smell as sweet." What does she mean by this?

  F Names can be confusing.

  G Names should appeal to the senses.

  H It is silly to give names to people and things.

  J A person or thing's name is unimportant.

3 The major conflict in this selection occurs mainly because of—

  A differences in cultures

  B differences in religion

  C differences between family members

  D differences between generations

4 Which is the literary point of view in this passage?

  F A third-person narrator describes the thoughts of several other people.

  G A first-person narrator describes her own thoughts and actions.

  H A third-person narrator describes the actions but not the thoughts of others.

  J A first-person narrator describes all the thoughts and actions of others.

Reading Comprehension

from "Hard as Nails" by Russell Baker

Directions:

Here is an excerpt from *Hard as Nails* **by Russell Baker. This essay describes Baker's first job—delivering newspapers in Baltimore. Read this excerpt. Then, complete numbers 5 and 6 by choosing the best answer.**

As we walked back to the house she [Baker's mother] said I couldn't have a paper route until I was twelve. And all because of some foolish rule they had down here in Baltimore. You'd think if a boy wanted to work they would encourage him instead of making him stay idle so long that laziness got embedded in his bones.

That was April. We had barely finished the birthday cake in August before Deems came by the apartment and gave me the tools of the newspaper trade: an account book for keeping track of the customers' bills and a long, brown web belt. Slung around one shoulder and across the chest, the belt made it easy to balance fifteen or twenty pounds of papers against the hip. I had to buy my own wire cutters for opening the newspaper bundles the trucks dropped at Wisengoff's store on the corner of Stricker and West Lombard streets.

In February my mother had moved us down from New Jersey, where we had been living with her brother Allen ever since my father died in 1930. This move of hers to Baltimore was a step toward fulfilling a dream. More than almost anything else in the world, she wanted "a home of our own." I'd heard her talk of that "home of our own" all through those endless Depression years when we lived as poor relatives dependent on Uncle Allen's goodness. "A home of our own. One of these days, Buddy, we'll have a home of our own."

That winter she had finally saved just enough to make her move, and she came to Baltimore. There were several reasons for Baltimore. For one, there were people she knew in Baltimore, people she could go to if things got desperate. And desperation was possible, because the moving would exhaust her savings, and the apartment rent was twenty-four dollars a month. She would have to find a job quickly. My sister Doris was only nine, but I was old enough for an after-school job that could bring home a few dollars a week. So as soon as it was legal I went into newspaper work.

5 **The author and his family moved to Baltimore because—**

    A his mother thought the rent was lower in Baltimore.

    B his mother wanted them to be near Doris.

    C his mother wanted them to have their own home.

    D his mother found a job in Baltimore.

6 **The author probably wrote this passage to—**

    F persuade children to get after-school jobs

    G show readers the unfairness of child labor

    H explain what it is like to live in Baltimore

    J entertain readers with a memory from his youth

Reading Comprehension

from *Talent* by Annie Dillard

Directions:

Read this excerpt from *Talent* by Annie Dillard. Then, complete numbers 7 and 8 by choosing the best answer.

There is no such thing as talent. If there are any inborn, God-given gifts, they are in the precocious fields of music, mathematics, and chess; if you have such a gift, you know it by now. All the rest of us, in all the other fields, are not talented. We all start out dull and weary and uninspired. Apart from a few like Mozart, there never have been any great and accomplished little children in the world. Genius is the product of education.

Perhaps it's a cruel thing to insist that there is no such thing as talent. We all want to believe—at least I do—that being selfless was "easy" for Albert Schweitzer, that Faulkner's novels just popped into his head, that Rembrandt painted because he "had to." We want to believe all these nonsensical things in order to get ourselves off the hook. For if these people had no talent, then might the rest of us have painting or writing or great thinking as an option? We, who have no talent? I think the answer is yes, absolutely.

---

7 What is the major purpose of this selection?

A to make a point about talent

B to persuade people to write novels

C to entertain with a story about talent

D to show why people are afraid of success

8 What does the writer mean when she says, "There is no such thing as talent"?

F People are rarely good at things.

G Nobody works hard anymore.

H People achieve great things through hard work.

J Nobody does things that are truly worthwhile.

Reading Comprehension

from "Becky and the Wheels-and-Brake Boys" by James Berry

Directions:

Read this excerpt from "Becky and the Wheels-and-Brake Boys" by James Berry. Then, complete numbers 9 and 10 by choosing the best answer.

Over and over I told my mum I wanted a bike. Over and over she looked at me as if I was crazy. "Becky, d'you think you're a boy? Eh? D'you think you're a boy? In any case, where's the money to come from? Eh?"

Of course I know I'm not a boy. Of course I know I'm not crazy. Of course I know all that's no reason why I can't have a bike. No reason! As soon as I get indoors I'll just have to ask again—ask Mum once more.

9 Which sentence best describes the literary point of view used in this passage?

A A third-person narrator describes the thoughts and actions of several other people.

B A first-person narrator describes only her own thoughts and actions.

C A first-person narrator describes her own thoughts and the actions of herself and others.

D A third-person narrator describes the action through the eyes of one person.

10 Becky's mother does not want her to have a bicycle because—

F she thinks only boys should ride bicycles.

G Becky does not do her chores.

H she wants Becky to watch her sister.

J Becky is too young.

Reading Comprehension

Directions:

Read this excerpt from a textbook. Then, complete number 11 by choosing the best answer.

The National Aeronautics and Space Administration (NASA) is responsible for running the United States space program. NASA's Project Mercury put the first Americans in space. This project also established NASA's ability to launch Earth-orbiting spacecraft. Project Apollo was designed to land Americans on the moon, a goal that was accomplished in July 1969 with the *Apollo 11* mission. Five additional lunar landings followed this success, ending with *Apollo 17* in 1972. As the space shuttle program continues, astronauts use their unique zero-gravity environment to conduct experiments and gather information for the benefit of earthbound humankind and future space travelers.

---

11 What is this passage mostly about?

   A future space travelers

   B the importance of the space shuttle

   C astronauts' specialized training

   D NASA's accomplishments

Reading Comprehension

Directions:

Read the following poster. Then, complete number 12 by choosing the best answer.

The Middle View Area Ski Club will hold

a Ski Trip to Silver Bells Ski Resort

on January 10

Students, friends, and family of all ages welcome!

Bus leaves the school at 8:30 A.M. and returns at 10:30 P.M.

Cost is $45 per person, including ski rental, lunch, and dinner.

Tickets are available at the school office.

The Ski Club needs your help! Students and parents need

to organize and supervise the trip.

Call Tony Parks at 555-2378 for more information.

---

12 Which of the following sentences from the poster is meant to persuade you to volunteer to organize the trip?

   F Tickets are available at the school office.

   G Call Tony Parks at 555-2378 for more information.

   H The Ski Club needs your help!

   J Bus leaves the school at 8:30 A.M. and returns at 10:30 P.M.

Spelling

Directions:

Read each group of sentences. For each item on the answer sheet, fill in the bubble for the answer that has a mistake in spelling. If there is no mistake, fill in the last answer choice.

1 A <u>Science</u> is Lee's favorite subject.

   B Are the <u>tomatoes</u> ripe yet?

   C Valentine's Day is in <u>Febuary</u>.

   D No mistake

2 F The <u>secetary</u> typed the letter.

   G Most kittens are <u>curious</u>.

   H <u>Whales</u> are mammals, not fish.

   J No mistake

3 A Lucy ate <u>ninety</u> peanuts.

   B The shirt was a <u>bargin</u> at $3.00.

   C <u>Parallel</u> lines never meet.

   D No mistake

4 F <u>Answer</u> all of the questions.

   G We will buy a new <u>calendar</u> in December.

   H Gary saw a movie at the <u>theater</u>.

   J No mistake

5 A They ate lunch in the <u>cafeteria</u>.

   B The next street is Sixth <u>Avenue</u>.

   C Did you take <u>medicin</u> for your cold?

   D No mistake

6 F Mom cooked <u>spagetti</u> and meatballs.

   G Darla's birthday is on <u>Wednesday</u>.

   H Would you like more mashed <u>potatoes</u>?

   J No mistake

7 A Luke <u>weighs</u> 85 pounds.

   B Is that word <u>misspelled</u>?

   C It takes <u>coperation</u> to succeed.

   D No mistake

8 F There was a <u>mysterious</u> noise in the woods.

   G The boys paddled the <u>canoe</u>.

   H In the fall the <u>leaves</u> change color.

   J No mistake

9 A It is <u>neccesary</u> to finish high school.

   B Sign the letter "Yours <u>truly</u>."

   C Winter is Bart's favorite <u>season</u>.

   D No mistake

10 F The fans shouted <u>encouragement</u> at the runners.

   G The puppy <u>excaped</u> from the yard.

   H Measure the <u>width</u> of the table.

   J No mistake

11 A <u>Abbreviate</u> Alabama as AL.

   B A drum is a <u>rythm</u> instrument.

   C That <u>restaurant</u> serves tacos.

   D No mistake

Spelling

12 **F** Do tests give you <u>anxiety</u>?

   G Pay the <u>cashier</u> for your lunch.

   H What is your <u>opinon</u> of rap music?

   J No mistake

13 **A** An eclipse will <u>ocurr</u> tomorrow.

   B Those <u>scissors</u> are very sharp.

   C A <u>nickel</u> equals five cents.

   D No mistake

14 **F** A <u>censis</u> counts all the people.

   G He ate ice cream for <u>dessert</u>.

   H The bride walked down the <u>aisle</u>.

   J No mistake

15 **A** Look up the word in a <u>dictionary</u>.

   B The Civil War was in the <u>ninteenth</u> century.

   C How old will you be in <u>ninety</u> years?

   D No mistake

16 **F** The ending of the book <u>satisfied</u> Selma.

   G The ending <u>surprised</u> Rita.

   H Brandon liked the <u>eighth</u> chapter best.

   J No mistake

17 **A** The flower garden is <u>beautiful</u>.

   B Let's take a <u>photograph</u> of the parade.

   C It is impolite to <u>interupt</u>.

   D No mistake

18 **F** 100 percent is the <u>maximum</u> score.

   G Read the <u>paragraf</u> about Mars.

   H Encyclopedia Brown is an <u>amateur</u> detective.

   J No mistake

19 **A** A chameleon's color is <u>changeable</u>.

   B Daily <u>exercise</u> helps make people healthy.

   C Give the dog a <u>biskit</u> as a treat.

   D No mistake

20 **F** Will you <u>persue</u> computers as a career?

   G The actors <u>rehearsed</u> the play.

   H Malik fell and <u>bruised</u> his knee.

   J No mistake

21 **A** The <u>physician</u> looked at Sue's tonsils.

   B Many scientists work in a <u>labertory</u>.

   C Return the books to the <u>library</u>.

   D No mistake

22 **F** The surprise party was a <u>sucess</u>.

   G The pyramids are <u>ancient</u> tombs.

   H A weather <u>satellite</u> orbits Earth.

   J No mistake

Language

Directions:

Read each passage. Then decide which type of error, if any, appears in each underlined section. For each item on the answer sheet, fill in the bubble for the answer. If there is no error, fill in the last answer choice.

The worlds largest library is the Library of Congress, which is in Washington, D.C.
1

The original library was burned by british troops during the War of 1812. The federal
2

government had very little money to build a new one, but a former president stepped in
3

to help. Thomas Jefferson, donated more than six thousand of his own books to get the
4

new library going. From this humble begining, the Library of Congress has grown to
5

include more than 20 million books, 10 million prints and photographs, and 4 million

atlases and maps. To hold these books, their are more than 530 miles of shelves.
6

---

1 A Spelling error

   B Capitalization error

   C Punctuation error

   D No error

2 F Spelling error

   G Capitalization error

   H Punctuation error

   J No error

3 A Spelling error

   B Capitalization error

   C Punctuation error

   D No error

4 F Spelling error

   G Capitalization error

   H Punctuation error

   J No error

5 A Spelling error

   B Capitalization error

   C Punctuation error

   D No error

6 F Spelling error

   G Capitalization error

   H Punctuation error

   J No error

Language

Many people believe, that animals cannot see colors, but this is not true. Dogs,
7

horses, and sheep are able to see some colors, although not as well as Humans can.
8

Monkeys are able to see colors, to. In fact, their color vision is almost equal to our own.
9

It is also obvious that birds' can see colors. There are different ways they attract other
10   11

birds, one of these ways is through their natural color.

But there are many animals that apparently cannot see colors. Bulls, for example, are
12

probly not excited by the color red in a bullfighter's cape. Instead, they are excited only
13

by the movement of the cape in the bullfighter's hands.

7 A Spelling error

    B Capitalization error

    C Punctuation error

    D No error

8 F Spelling error

    G Capitalization error

    H Punctuation error

    J No error

9 A Spelling error

    B Capitalization error

    C Punctuation error

    D No error

10 F Spelling error

    G Capitalization error

    H Punctuation error

    J No error

11 A Spelling error

    B Capitalization error

    C Punctuation error

    D No error

12 F Spelling error

    G Capitalization error

    H Punctuation error

    J No error

13 A Spelling error

    B Capitalization error

    C Punctuation error

    D No error

Language

Directions:

Read the passage. Then, choose the word or group of words that belongs in each space. For each item on the answer sheet, fill in the bubble for the answer that you think is correct.

The writer Bailey White has an ____(1)____ story to tell of how, as a child, she hatched sixteen wild turkeys! White's mother had long been a friend of local ornithologists, or bird experts. The ornithologists were worried that the wild turkey was headed for extinction [dying out]. When they found a nest of eggs, they could hardly control their excitement. They camped out in the woods to protect the ____(2)____ nest from people or animals that might harm it. Unfortunately, however, they scared off the mother turkey, and she ____(3)____ her nest on the night the eggs were supposed to hatch.

Six-year-old Bailey White was suffering from a case of the measles and a temperature that ____(4)____ to 102 degrees. She barely remembers the ornithologists creeping into ____(5)____ room with a cardboard box, but she remembers very clearly what happened the next morning. When she woke up, the little girl was surprised to find sixteen baby turkeys ____(6)____ her bed! White helped take care of the turkeys until one day in late summer. Then, with the ornithologists and White ____(7)____ watching, the wild turkeys were set free.

---

1 **A** interested
   B interesting
   C interest
   D interests

2 **F** rarest
   G rarer
   H rare
   J rarely

3 **A** abandoned
   B would have abandoned
   C abandoning
   D was abandoned

4 **F** had risen
   G will rise
   H rises
   J is rising

5 **A** their
   B her
   C she
   D our

6 **F** sharing
   G are sharing
   H share
   J shares

7 **A** most careful
   B careful
   C carefully
   D more careful

Language

Directions:

Read each passage. Some sections are underlined. The underlined sections may be one of the following:
- **Incomplete sentences**
- **Run-on sentences**
- **Correctly written sentences that should be combined**
- **Correctly written sentences that do not need to be rewritten**

Choose the best way to write each underlined section and mark the letter for your answer. If the underlined section needs no change, mark the choice "Correct as is."

Without the hard work of Noah Webster. We might never have had spelling bees!
8

In the early days of the United States no uniform spelling of words existed. Webster
9   10

changed all that with his *American Dictionary of the English Language.* It was published
11

in 1828. It included 70,000 words.

---

8 F Without the hard work of Noah Webster, we might never have had spelling bees!

G Without the hard work. Of Noah Webster we might never have had spelling bees!

H Without the hard work of Noah Webster, which we might never have had spelling bees!

J Correct as is

9 A In the early days of the United States. No uniform spelling of words existed.

B In the early days of the United States, no uniform spelling of words existed.

C No uniform spelling of words existed until the early days of the United States.

D Correct as is

10 F Webster changed all that. With his *American Dictionary of the English Language.*

G Webster, changed all that, with his *American Dictionary of the English Language.*

H Changing all that, Webster did with his *American Dictionary of the English Language.*

J Correct as is

11 A It was published in 1828 and the dictionary also included 70,000 words.

B Published in 1828, it included 70,000 words.

C It was published in 1828, it included 70,000 words.

D Correct as is

Language

It was spring of the year 1836. The Texas Revolution had been going on for several
<u>12</u>

months. It had started in October 1835. Many lives had already been lost. The Texans
<u>13</u>

had suffered a serious defeat at the Alamo mission. The Alamo was a mission in San

Antonio. The 189 men there had fought against more than 3,000 Mexican troops, and
<u>14</u>

every one of them had died in the battle.

On April 21, 1836, the Texans' luck turned when Sam Houston's army crept up on

the Mexican troops near the San Jacinto River. There they sprang a surprise attack.
<u>15</u>

Which turned out to be more successful than they had imagined. The Battle of San

Jacinto lasted less than 20 minutes and ended when the Texans captured the Mexican

leader, Santa Anna. In return for setting him free, the Texans demanded their immediate
<u>16</u>

independence. The Mexican leader had little choice but to agree. A treaty was quickly

signed. Texas was no longer part of Mexico it was an independent country.
<u>17</u>

12 F The Texas Revolution had been going on for several months, it had started in October 1835.

   G The Texas Revolution had started in October 1835 and the Texas Revolution had been going on for several months.

   H The Texas Revolution, which had started in October 1835, had been going on for several months.

   J Correct as is

13 A The Alamo was a mission in San Antonio, which Texans had suffered a serious defeat there.

   B The Texans had suffered a serious defeat at the Alamo mission in San Antonio.

   C Suffering a serious defeat, the Alamo was a mission in San Antonio.

   D Correct as is

Language

14 F The 189 men there had fought against more than 3,000 Mexican troops, every one of them had died in the battle.

G The 189 men there had fought. Against more than 3,000 Mexican troops, who had all died in the battle.

H Against more than 3,000 troops were what the 189 men had fought against and died there.

J Correct as is

15 A There they sprang a surprise attack and the surprise attack turned out to be more successful than they had imagined.

B There they sprang a surprise attack, which turned out to be more successful than they had imagined.

C They were more successful than they had imagined. When they sprang a surprise attack there.

D Correct as is

16 F In return for setting him free. The Texans demanded their immediate independence.

G In return, the Texans demanded their immediate independence, for setting him free.

H The Texans demanded their immediate independence, in return they set him free.

J Correct as is

17 A Texas was no longer part of Mexico; it was an independent country.

B Texas was no longer part of Mexico and Texas was an independent country.

C Texas, no longer part of Mexico, an independent country.

D Correct as is

Language

Directions:

Read the following questions. Then, complete number 18 by choosing the best answer.

18 Suppose that you are writing an essay comparing your favorite class and your least favorite class. Which of the following organizers would be most useful?

    F time line

    G cause-effect frame

    H Venn diagram

    J character-change map

Directions:

Kenny is working on an essay about his pet hamster. Several mistakes need to be corrected. Read the following paragraph. Then, complete numbers 19 through 21 by choosing the best answer.

[1]When my brother and I asked our parents for a pet, we were hoping for a dog, so we were disappointed when our father bought us a hamster, but we weren't sad for long. [2]Sammy is our hamster. [3]Sammy is really cute. [4]He also spends a lot of time digging. [5]My father told my brother and me that Sammy does this because hamsters dig burrows in the wild. [6]Sammy is the most lovable hamster I have ever seen. [7]He loves to come out of his cage and be held. [8]Sometimes he crawls up my arm, onto my shoulder, and nibbles my ear. [9]Show me a dog do that!

19 Which of these best combines Sentences 2 and 3 into one?

    A Sammy is our hamster, but he is really cute.

    B Sammy is our hamster and really cute.

    C Sammy is our hamster; Sammy is really cute.

    D Sammy, our hamster, is really cute.

20 Which sentence should be rewritten as two complete sentences?

    F Sentence 1

    G Sentence 5

    H Sentence 6

    J Sentence 7

21 If Kenny wanted to add a paragraph to his essay, a good topic would be

    A what hamsters eat

    B what kind of dog Kenny wants

    C why hamsters are cute

    D who takes care of Sammy

Listening

Directions:

Suppose that the following paragraph is being read aloud. Read the paragraph. Then, complete numbers 1 and 2 by choosing the best answer.

My first apartment in New York was in a <u>gritty</u> warehouse district, the kind of place that makes your parents wince. A lot of old Italians lived around me, which suited me just fine because I was the granddaughter of old Italians. Their own children and grandchildren had moved to Long Island and New Jersey. All they had was me. All I had was them.

—from "Melting Pot" by Anna Quindlen

1 You can tell from the passage that the word <u>gritty</u> means—

A tough

B lovely

C urban

D old

2 This passage gives you enough information to believe that the speaker and her neighbors—

F were related by blood

G got on each other's nerves

H grew up in New Jersey and then moved to New York City

J became important to each other

Listening

Directions:

The Brentwood School Board decided to require student athletes to attend physical education (P.E.) classes. Sandra delivered the following speech during a class debate. Read the paragraph. Then, complete numbers 3 through 5 by choosing the best answer.

> Playing a team sport at school requires the same type of physical activity as a P.E. course. Athletes may exhaust or injure themselves if they take part in both activities. In addition, the time spent in P.E. courses can be put to use by coaches as training time. That way, athletes would not have to spend so much time training after school and would have more time to study. Finally, as I understand it, P.E. courses are supposed to develop an interest in athletics. Students who take part in team sports already have this interest. For athletes, P.E. is unnecessary, and it might even be harmful—both physically and academically.

3 **What does Sandra mean when she says that P.E. classes could be academically harmful for athletes?**

A P.E. classes would be difficult for athletes, and they might fail.

B P.E. classes take up time that athletes could use to study for their other classes.

C Athletes who take P.E. classes would have to drop out of one of their other courses.

D P.E. classes would create too much homework for athletes.

4 **This speech was given in order to—**

F complain about athletic teams

G explain why the school board should change its decision

H explain why the school board should not change its decision

J express the school board's opinions about its decision

5 **Suppose that while listening to Sandra's speech, you had to write her words. Which of the following would be the best listening technique?**

A listening to the first sentence of the speech

B listening for information in the speech that you find interesting

C listening for the most important points of the speech

D listening to the last sentence of the speech